What people are saying about Do

W hat doctors Matola and Johns[ ] book, *Don't Pull The Plug*, is shine tne spotlight on our indomitable spirit. They have given all of us, regardless of our physical abilities, a bold reminder of what Goethe said, "Whatever you can do, or dream, you can begin it, because boldness has genius, power and magic in it." This book is indeed a "stroke of genius."

—*Dr. Stan Dale, Founder and director,*
Human Awareness Institute
Author, *Fantasy Can Set You Free*

D r. Matola succeeds at getting into the heart and soul of the personal issues related to post-stroke rehabilitation with this compilation of his many insightful essays. Over the years that I have known Tom, I was quite fortunate to have had the opportunity to work with him on a variety of research projects related to locomotor control after stroke. Although we initially began working to better understand how the nervous system recovers its ability to control movement after stroke, I soon realized that Tom was teaching me much more about humanistic ramification of stroke.

Most of all, Tom reminds those of us in the health care profession that each person who recovers from stroke is an individual with thoughts, emotions, and feelings that must be acknowledged and appreciated. The hopes, dreams, fears, and motivating factors described in this book will provide inspiration for others who will themselves be faced with the sudden reality of challenged abilities.

—*David Brown, Ph.D.,*
Northwestern University Medical School, Chicago, Illinois
Asst. Professor in PT and Physical Movement

Thomas and Roberta have demonstrated to me, both through how they live, and now by writing this honest book, four powerful elements in experiencing a meaningful life. These are courage, commitment, concern for others, and love.

Their experiences flow powerfully through each essay. During their encounters with challenges they have not lost their sense of humor. Their ability to write in such a warm and direct manner has helped me gain a new appreciation for my life and for others who are challenged in their own personal ways. This book ought to infuse the four elements into the lives of all who read these poignant and life-affirming words. This book is *a toast to life.*

—*David Leopold Schwartz, Ph.D.,*
International University, Summit University

Here is a fresh look on a new life, and a refreshing outlook for creating a new philosophy, after a experiencing a life altering change. Tom has presented a positive philosophy that puts one in balance.

—*Joan Worley M.S., Adaptive P.E. Coordinator,*
Instructor, West Valley Junior College,
Saratoga, CA

Don't Pull the Plug is a celebration of life and the indomitable human spirit. This book is a witty, sincere, and at times humorous account of one courageous man's journey through life, its struggles, and its accomplishments. It is a must for anyone who needs an uplift draft to carry her through each day's trials and tribulations. Each section—no, each page clearly and cleverly offers its readers hope and inspiration, along with innumerable reasons to keep going on. Buy. Read it, and Love it. It will make you cry and make you laugh hysterically!

—**Sharon Janus,** *Equestrian and Educator*
Author, *Magic of Horses: Horses as Healers*

Don't Pull The Plug

A Lesson In Life

A collection of essays about a stroke,
rehabilitation, empowerment, living and
dying, cats, spiders, horses, aliens,
And, of course ... Sex.

Thomas Matola, Ph.D.
Roberta Johnson, J.D.

Intrepid Press
Los Gatos, California

Body text is set in 11 point Bitstream Iowan Oldstyle and heads are set in ITC Kabel. Cover and interior design by Pete Masterson, Æonix Publishing Group, www.aeonix.com.

Library of Congress Control Number: 2001097060

ISBN 0-9714918-0-1

Published by

Intrepid Press
PMB 142
15559 Union Avenue
Los Gatos, CA 95032-3904

FAX: 408-559-8212
PH: 408-559-4440
E-MAIL: iintrepids@aol.com
WEB SITE: www.dontpulltheplug.net

Printed in the United States of America

This book is dedicated
To all who have survived a stroke
To all who are living with a disability, and
To their caregivers
With love

Thomas Matola, Ph.D.
San Jose, California
2001

Table of Photos

Contents

Section IV: Attitudes

Section V: Musings

Conclusion

Appendices

Special Thanks to

Chris Baer, friend, personal assistant, driver, handyman around the house, floral arranger.

Michael Bremer, consultant.

Lenora Bolyard, secretary and interpreter of the authors' illegible writing.

Ann Carruthers, friend, proofreader, data organizer, and much more.

Lisa DeVos, daughter extraordinary.

Becky Levine, editor.

Pepita Carrion Rebelo, friend, ray of sunshine, before and after.

Pete Masterson, Æonix Publishing Group, consultant, designer, typesetter and our "answer man."

Deedee Shute, friend and angel.

Introduction

In order to get to what will be,
You need to be willing to go through
What was and
Be with what is.

Fear is an illusion.
If you use the same
Energy to be confident
Wonderful things
Will happen.

—FRANKLIN DELANO ROSEVELT

I did not set out to write this book! It just happened. Like the stroke just happened. Out of the blue it came. The stroke hit suddenly. But the book idea evolved over the years. Those years were spent in recovering, accepting, learning, and grieving. In that process, I started writing. After I learned to type with one hand, I began to talk to my computer about my feelings, my joys, and my pain. I discovered I had many questions.

My search for the meaning of life as a disabled person took me on a jagged time line, exploring my past, assessing my present, and daring to dream about my future.

I wanted to reach others in my situation. After all, I spent most of my life as a teacher. So my musings on the computer became articles which were published.

This book of mine is a collection of these articles. It is not a diary. It is not a journal. It is a collection. It is an album, if you will, picturing the musings of one who has been there, done that, and still wants to keep doing it. This is about a new lifestyle. It is about getting on with it. It is about continuing to be productive. It is most of all, about living!

I have shared stories with my disabled peers. I know my story is their story. I tell it here for all of us to share, to instruct, to console, to cajole, and to reach out to others. I present it in no particular order. The dates mentioned are correct as of the date the article was published. It is a sampler. Taste of it what you will. Although I have grouped the essays into separate categories, you may want to dip into them at your whim or will. Use whatever works. Then pass it on to a friend.

My partner, Roberta "Bobby" Johnson, has been a steadfast caregiver from the beginning. As a former journalist, she has contributed her expertise to the writing and editing of this book.

Barbara Heine and Sharon Janus, experts in their own fields, have graciously granted permission to reprint their articles.

Any errors or omissions are the responsibility of the principal authors.

Section I: The Beginning

People are always blaming their circumstances
for what they are.

I don't believe in circumstances.

The people who get on in this world
are the people who get up and look for
the circumstances they want, and,
if the can't find them, make them.

—GEORGE BERNARD SHAW

The authors before the stroke

Acceptance Does Not Mean Defeat

I have observed that a question is often more important than an answer. Only with the right question can there be any hope of finding the right answer.

I have also observed, as a stroke survivor, that I often ask myself these questions: Why me? Why did I have a stroke?

In the four years since the "incident" I have gone around and around with that particular question and found no answer that really satisfied. Only recently, I broke through to another question and, in retrospect, it seems so simple I wonder why I never asked it before.

The new question became: Since I have had a stroke and I am the way I am, still in a wheelchair and still with my right side impaired, is there any reason for me to be a survivor? That question engendered others: Are there lessons to be learned? Is it my cosmic karma to now pay for past wrongs? Is there a positive side?

I have concluded that I cannot know for sure and, therefore, I can choose. So I have decided to go forward. My mission is to continue my former life as a teacher. I now only teach about life, an active life for the disabled.

My experience taught me about doctors and therapists. There were those who were afraid to hold out hope because there was no guarantee of meaningful recovery. They didn't want to offer me false hope. But denying any hope negated the possibility of recovery. Even if there were not much physical recovery, the mind and spirit need to be nurtured. In the very act of trying to recover, recovery happens.

In my own case, I do several things that frighten me. I ride a horse. I am scared to death of horses. But for two years now I have gone each week for therapy on that huge animal. I still don't walk, but I certainly sit straight, have great strength in my unaffected side and improved tone in the other.

I swim several times a week. I am not afraid of water, but I am afraid of taking it into my lungs. However the exercise has helped my breathing and has kept me limber.

The practice of overcoming fear gives me great confidence. And improvement in mobility and flexibility keeps happening.

Six months after the stroke hit, when I still needed a "gait" belt and a strap to keep me upright in my chair, my doctor told me it was all over for me, that my condition was now stable! That devastated me for several days. Then I fought back. When the doctor said the reason for this prognosis was that statistics showed there was little recovery after six months, I said the statistics did not reflect the individual achievement. In the face of my determination, my doctor backed down. I continued to receive my medical benefits and more therapy. I kept showing signs of improvement. To this day, I keep improving. The gains seem small but over a period of time, they add up. Looking back, I can see they are truly large gains.

Not long ago, after my speech therapist said there was no more to be done, I found a different therapist. She had new methods. She recommended a breathing therapist who found I was not using my lungs properly. After a short period of treatment, I learned to breathe in the new way. For the first time in four years, I was able to deliver a full lecture to a large audience at a local hospital, without needing a microphone. I had come from no voice, using an alphabet card for the first three months to speaking loudly and clearly to a roomful of patients.

So, from those therapists who believed in "never say die," I learned to keep going. And to those who were naysayers, I became a teacher. To those who were afraid to raise "false hopes," I demonstrated that acceptance of my condition did not mean defeat. Accepting means taking the condition as the basis and going on from there. Hope and faith must be maintained.

It is self-defeating to cop out to accepting without hope. To say my karma brought it on and there's nothing to do about it is opting for failure. Better to say my karma has brought me a new opportunity and go from there.

I am reminded of a story: The man who broke his arm asked his doctor if he would be able to play the violin when the arm healed. The doctor assured him he could. The man smiled and said, "That is good, because I never could play the violin before."

I don't expect to play the violin. But I do expect to keep trying. So if I consider that life gave me lemons when it gave me the stroke, I'll just keep looking for recipes to make lemonade and drink a toast to life!

Dying to Live

I was near death. I did not ask for it. Nevertheless, I was there. It happened suddenly. No warning. The symptoms that brought me to the Kaiser Santa Theresa emergency room did not seem near fatal. I could not control a sudden dizziness. The medical people did not seem worried. They gave me something to take and were about to send me home, when it hit.

The first stroke was swift but mild. The second, coming soon after, was severe. When I awoke, I saw dozens of scopes, tubes, and meters connected to different parts of my body. I was taking oxygen through my nose. I watched the blips on the screens. Sometimes I felt like an astronaut in outer space, measuring where and how I was by the feedback on the computers. Sometimes I felt I was a character in a television hospital show. I was not sure if a blip was good or bad. I knew that if I got a straight line I was dead.

But where was the tunnel of light? Where were my departed friends and family? I did not review my whole life, but I felt fear. I suddenly knew I could die, and I knew I was very close.

Once, a long time ago, I did past-lives regression. I had out-of-body experiences. Now, in the hospital critical care unit, I felt as if I was an observer looking at my body and at the people tending me. I did not feel like a participant.

I remember thinking about my purpose in life. Was there

any reason for me to continue taking up space here on earth? To say there wasn't did not sound right to me. I thought there must be a reason to keep on living. It was the first time I questioned my existence. Until that time I always felt immortal. But in that intensive care area, my doctor asked me about "pulling the plug" on my life support systems. In a flash, I realized I was going to die right then if I did not do something. At that point, there was no time to find out what my purpose in life was.

I was afraid. I was angry, too. I do not know where the anger came from, but I did not like my doctor asking his question. The anger and fear did not leave, but I started fighting the blood loss, the fever, and all the other dangerous conditions. Now it was the equipment and me fighting to stay alive. The fear was great. I was afraid to sleep. I stayed up all night, night after long night, for a long time. I watched TV. Occasionally I convinced myself I was not going to die, and then I could sleep for a few hours.

I knew I needed some strong motivation to keep on living. The only thing that fit at the time was anger. I could not feel anything else, not even love. I had spent many years studying and practicing meditation, tai chi, the Tao. I tried to "go with the flow." I tried "letting go." I tried giving up control. I could not. All I could do was live with the fear. I could not breathe on my own. I was losing blood. I was choking. I was afraid of aspirating. Every small, previously unconscious bodily function was a struggle. I lost my feeling of immortality. I was in a battle for survival.

As the weeks rolled by, and as some of the fear of imminent death faded, I began to think of how to bring order to my new life situation. I had regained some strength and some speech ability. I dictated an article. Before my stroke I had been working on my doctoral degree. I had planned to write my thesis on aging and sex. Now I wrote about sex and a stroke. I had it published and taped a copy above my bed in the rehabilitation facility. This helped me turn my thoughts away from dying and more to living. After all, sex was fun, and love was the basis of good living and a good life. I no longer thought only of survival.

Until that time I had put my purpose for living on hold. I lived with the anger. I asked, "Why me?" After all, I had been a healthy person. I had none of the risk factors for stroke. I was not overweight. I did not smoke. I did not drink. I exercised. I was even exploring God. So why me?

It took a while, but I finally got the answer. It was simple. It did not matter why I had the stroke. What mattered was what I was going to do now. Just because I was near death did not mean I could not get back to life. I was not going to stop living. If I survived, it meant I had been given more time. I began to think about what I would now do with this gift.

I have decided I want to serve others, to help them get on with their lives. My body has limited ability to get around, but my mind is free and agile. I decided to finish my schooling, and I earned my doctorate as a sexologist. I lecture and write now. I specialize in what I know best. From personal and professional experience, I deal with the subjects of aging, disability, and sex. My rewards are many. I have made new friends, gone to new places, and I do new things. While I cannot hike, I can accompany my loved ones while they walk and I ride in my scooter.

As I began doing more, I also began exploring more within me. I wanted to know more about an afterlife. I have studied religious and spiritual ideas. I had looked into the theory of reincarnation. I was raised in the Catholic Church, and I knew about heaven and hell after death. Judaism offered divergent views. What should I pick? I chose to believe in reincarnation.

My mind also traveled to other worlds. While I still believed I was going to die, I considered the possibility of disappearing from this planet and going to live on another. Why not? I was still confused. For even though I think I know that reincarnation is real, I am still afraid that I may be wrong about it. I have read that energy never dies and that our life force energy cannot end. There has to be a continuation. That theory makes sense to me. Psychics have told me that I am an old soul. I have many past lives and I am ready for a higher level. Does that mean heaven? Does that mean another planet? I think of Jesus Christ who said what he could do as the son of God, man could do better.

Recently I attended a conference called "Living Well and Dying Well." I listened to stories of people who picked their time of death. Others told of death being a birth. It was a change-of-state, a re-birthing. Death remains a mystery. No speaker at the conference admitted to anything other than "not knowing."

That is all right with me. It comes back to what we know, and what we know is that we are alive and can live in this moment. I know I live now. My brush with death has shown me the way. I salute both life and death. In the meantime I say, along with Tevye in the *Fiddler on the Roof*: " To Life!"

Overcoming Fear:
A Stroke Survivor's Conflict

Until the stroke in 1991, I had a normal reaction to fear. I was afraid of hot stoves, of being mugged, and of horses, to name a few. But the stroke marked the beginning of fears I had never dreamed were possible in my life.

I became afraid to move, even though I knew I had limited mobility. I was afraid to be alone, although I knew I had help nearby. I was afraid to talk, although I knew I was becoming intelligible. In short, I became afraid to live. I should mention I was also becoming afraid to die.

As a psychologist who had dealt with paranoid clients in the past, I knew what was realistic and what was not. When I examined my fears, I recognized their inherent validity. I had a right to be afraid!

What to do about it? Should I be a turtle? Or should I be a hare? Being a turtle meant I would move more safely, but it would be slow. Being a hare meant taking leaps, and maybe, I thought, that was reckless.

I decided I wanted to live, to truly live. I wanted to be out there in the world. As the song said, I wanted to be all that I could be. I determined I would learn to deal with the razor's edge and find a way. There had to be a way to take the risks necessary to make progress in rehabilitation and recovery. After all, the world we live in, both the abled and the disabled, is scary. It is full of hazards, pitfalls, and failures. It is dangerous to our physical and psychological health. There is pollution, bigotry, violence, corruption, greed, and crime. But there are rewards. That's life.

So I had to deal with fear. How would I do it in this hostile world, made even more so by my disability? I decided I did not want to hide from the fear. I would not retreat into my turtle shell. I knew the world was not a bowl of cherries, and I, as a disabled person, decided I was not the pits.

Is fear a four-letter word? If so, then I must get to the root of the word. Like those other four-letter words, it is best not to say them in society, but it wise to know what they mean and to know that, as the general semanticists taught, the word is not the act. However, beyond the word there was the emotion. That was real. The loss of my control left by the stroke was also real.

What I learned was that dealing with the fear, doing something the first time with the fear, lessened the fear. I then accepted that as a mantra. I can, I said, now control my mind to know I am afraid and to do it anyway, with the help of my friends.

So I convinced myself to start taking the steps I needed to get back out in the world of the living. Before my stroke, I loved the water and I loved to swim. Now swim therapy was an order and I was frightened. I recognized that fear. What was real about the fear was that I could aspirate water into my lungs. What to do? I took as deep a breath as I could then manage and hung on to my therapist. Each day was a trial, but each day brought me closer to accepting. I still cannot swim as I used to, but I can and do enjoy the walk in the water and the exercises. And certainly, I enjoy the added strength and confidence it gives me.

Before my stroke, I was afraid of horses. I am still afraid of horses, but now I ride a horse weekly for therapy. The reality of the fear is there. Horses are huge animals, and it is a long way to fall from their back. I stay with the fear but stay closer to the pot of gold at the end of the rainbow. I have better posture, increased pelvic control, more range of motion in my arms and legs, more confidence in myself. Again, I stayed with fear and stayed close to my therapists. I think what I am saying is that I started to develop, along with the fear, a trust in my trainers and friends to be there when I needed them.

I would give anything not to have had the stroke. But since there is no payoff in that attitude, I now look for the positive. It is not that I like facing fear, but having had to do it has made a difference.

I have had time to reflect on fear and my fears in particular. As a child and as an adult, I had a fear of heights. I joined the Air Force anyway. I remembered that my fear didn't have to stop me. I even enjoyed flying the plane upside down. But I am still afraid of Ferris wheels. So what? I can and do stay away from them.

On reflection, I began to see that fear is a perception and, as such, can be controlled. We can assess the reality of it and take steps to avoid it where it is too great or not needed. Where necessary, we can take steps to modify the fear and to get it into our control. Where we can, we control the danger itself, and that lessens the fear.

Other things I am afraid of include pain, being unloved, being alone, and being ignored. I am also afraid of dying, I think, because I do not know what comes after. I have been afraid of different things at different times in my life. As a child, I was afraid of growing up. As a teenager, I was afraid of the future: would I go to college, would I marry, would I have kids? What about sex? All these things were scary for me. I had a fear of poverty for a while. I still cope with fears of growing old, of not being useful. I worry that I cannot serve mankind, nature, and do some good work while I am on this earth.

With the stroke came new fears. Since I could not talk for a while, I worried about being understood. This was especially frightening for me since all my life I had been a "talker." My profession as a teacher depended on speech. I had to learn to keep trying no matter how apprehensive

I felt. Walking presented another fear. I was afraid of falling. I walk a bit now, and I do it with the fear, although I find the fear diminishes as I get on with the task. Although I see improvement in my condition even after seven years, I become afraid that I will not make any additional progress. I also fear getting sick and having to go to a convalescent hospital.

The list of fears can be endless, but I have come to know that. I have also come to know that the list of possibilities is also endless. I acknowledge the fears now. I now know that it is easier to deal with fear than to become its slave. I like to think of fear as one more tool, an empowerment if you will, in my search for a full life.

Stroke: A Bird's Eye View

In early September 1991, I was a healthy man, working in my profession as a college instructor and enjoying the opera on vacation in Santa Fe, when a spider bit me. I later learned it was a deadly brown recluse spider. Only immediate medical treatment saved me. I seemed to recover, but two weeks later, home in California, I lost my balance because of severe dizziness. I was treated for labyrinthitis and was about to be released when, in front of my family and my doctor, right there in the emergency room, I had a stroke. (To this day I believe that spider bite caused the stroke. The doctors don't know and won't say.)

The first stroke was mild, but two days later, a second one hit. This one was major. I almost didn't make it. My doctor was considering taking me off life support, but I refused. Even though I was unable to speak, I conveyed my determination to live. I remember it as a conscious decision. And live I did.

The experience inspired me. Fighting to live served me well when it came to recovering. I learned it was my choice. I was hospitalized for four months. I had good medical care all that time. What I didn't have was good information on how to recover. Mostly, the medical personnel believed that after six months, nothing new in the way of improvement could happen. It was then I learned that I had to take charge of my own recovery. I had to do the research myself.

The first six months I spent in Sacramento, California, where my partner was then living and working. My medical carrier authorized occupational, physical, and speech therapy. I made some improvement. I learned how to eat and how to begin using my voice again. But the improvement was slow and painstaking.

I wanted more. I started asking what other options were available. I heard about water therapy and enrolled in a swimming program. I joined a class for stroke survivors in which we did range-of-motion exercises. In those days, I needed a belt to keep me in my chair.

These programs let me see that I wasn't paralyzed. I was just weak. That realization bolstered my confidence that I could strengthen my muscles. Also, I started listening to others. I heard all the "war stories." Most impressive was the similarity of other survivors' experience. People told about being given up by their doctors, of being told they would not improve. But they did. The director of the water therapy program, a young woman named Suzy, had spent 7 years in a wheelchair after a car accident when she was 17. The doctors told her she would never walk again. She finally decided to start swimming. With perseverance she became a champion swimmer, regained the use of her legs, and—when I knew her—at age 30, she was not only walking, but running marathons and learning to ski.

When we moved back to San Jose, I had to find available programs. A lot of digging led to all of the activities I had access to in Sacramento, and more. A major plus was the opportunity to socialize and meet new friends. These connections also provided leads to other innovative approaches to stroke recovery.

I heard about ongoing experimental programs run by Stanford University and the Veterans Administration. I was accepted into one and was involved as a "lab rat" for many years. The director of the program, Dr. David Brown, now at Northwestern University, had devised a bicycle that was hooked up to computers. I rode this bicycle and a biofeedback screen told us the output of energy from each of my legs. After many months, I was able to control this energy flow, primarily by just thinking about it, so that I gave equal energy to each leg. This has strengthened my legs, and I am hopeful I will be able to walk in the future.

As I learned of new programs and if I thought they might help, I tried them. Some did, some didn't. But my motto is "Nothing ventured, nothing gained." These programs included herbal remedies and acupuncture. And just because they didn't work for me, doesn't mean they wouldn't work for somebody else.

I find massage helpful, but changed from gentle massage to a deep sports-type treatment. I have been a "lab rat" for other therapy programs. They call me when they are having a teaching session. I go, and they demonstrate on me.

The most challenging therapy I am engaged in is riding a horse. My partner's family is involved in horse therapy for disabled persons. At first, I couldn't sit up straight. I hunched over, and the assistants had to hold me up. It was hard, going back week after week, but I did it, and finally I was beginning to enjoy my ride.

But the work there was more recreational than therapeutic and it was suggested I go to the National Center for Equestrian Facilitated Therapy in Woodside, California. Physical therapists run this program. I was evaluated by them, and they determined I could probably benefit from their therapy.

Two different horse therapy programs helped me. Still a bit afraid, I now ride without hands on the reins. I can stand up in the saddle and can trot not only in the ring, but cross-country as well. The therapists installed a hoist for getting me on the horse. I sit in this canvas sling, and they lift me onto the horse. What a thrill! What a wonderful feeling of accomplishment, especially when I feed my horse a carrot after we are through riding.

Recently, I felt there might be something more out there that would help me and I asked my doctor for additional therapy. He authorized speech therapy. The new therapist found new ways to help. She told me my palate had dropped and gave me a simple exercise that did improve my ability to talk. She noted I was not breathing properly and referred me to a specialist in that field. I relearned how to use my lungs and have improved enough so that I can now return to lecturing. I want to emphasize that it is important to try new things, and even go back to old therapies to see if there are new ideas and new developments.

After my stroke, I not only finished my studies in a doctoral program, but I was awarded my Ph.D. in Sexology. I have written and published several articles, contributed chapters to two books and am engaged in publishing my own book.

All the therapies have helped me get better physically, emotionally, and psychologically. I am enjoying my life. Life is worth living. I go to the opera. I go to plays and movies and go often. I travel. I visit with friends and family. I garden. That is, I plan the gardens and Chris, my personal assistant, helps do the heavy work. I have an herb garden that I use a lot in cooking, another hobby of mine.

Since I intend to specialize in writing and lecturing about sexuality and disability, I spend a lot of time researching strokes. It helps professionally, but it is also self-serving, since I learn about new things I may do to help myself even more.

I still get depressed and discouraged. But then I recall the way I was at the beginning, and I see where I am now, and I am heartened. I love life. I know life must go on, and if it can't go on the way it was, then there is another lifestyle for me. I can adapt, find new ways, and do what I can do.

Spider Bites and Stroke

Spider bites can cause strokes! Unlikely? Perhaps. But who knows? We used to think the world was flat. We used to think the mind and the body was separate. Maybe there is a connection, and maybe we should explore it.

I have no proof my spider bite caused my stroke, although I wonder about it. To wonder is the beginning of finding the truth. I believe it is time to share our stories, and maybe someone out there will find answers.

Here's my story: Five years ago, while on an opera tour in Santa Fe, New Mexico, I suddenly felt severe pain in my leg. Just as suddenly, my leg swelled to double its size. I rushed to the hospital. The triage nurse took one look and ordered immediate treatment.

I had no idea what it was. The Santa Fe doctors did. A recluse spider had bitten me. The doctors had seen this kind of bite on other patients; the bite was frequently deadly. I was lucky. They treated me and advised me to have my doctor follow up when I returned home. My doctor could find no reason to continue treating because the swelling had subsided. The open sore had healed.

At the time I thought I was lucky. Now I am not so sure. Two weeks later I was rushed to the emergency room of my local hospital. I was experiencing extreme labyrinthitis. Several hours later, still in the emergency room, I suffered a stroke.

Was there a connection between the spider bite and the stroke? All the medical people I asked denied the possibility, or shrugged it off, saying it was not likely.

I have never been easy with the response. I have always been allergic to insect bites. A centipede got me a few years earlier while I was visiting the Mojave Desert. Quick treatment took care of the painful swelling. Ordinary mosquitoes and fleas bite me and I react with swelling and pain. The recluse spider's bite was the worst I had ever suffered. Friends suggested it might have caused a blood clot that traveled to my brain two weeks later.

Maybe it was the bite. This explanation is as likely as any, since I had none of the risk factors for stroke. I did not smoke or drink. I was not overweight. I was generally calm. I did yoga, tai chi, and meditated.

I keep wondering. I read about a person who suffered a recluse spider bite and did not get quick treatment. She lost her arms and legs. Maybe if we explored the possibility, and kept open minds, we would learn there was a connection. Then we could take steps to avoid the clot that could travel to the brain. We could think of this risk the way we think of auto accidents, or AIDS. Maybe the best cure is prevention.

The medical researchers could talk cross specialty. Those studying bugs could talk to those studying plants in the rain forest, for example. There are poisons in some plants and animals that can be turned into cures for diseases. I remember Mother used snake poison for her heart problems. The Indians ingested poison oak to prevent being infected.

Today we have the miracle of instant communication on the Internet. Each of us with our own personal "little" story could share with others. If we all wondered a lot and talked a lot about our problems and theories, we could probably find the answers. Why not?

On Taking Risks

To risk, or not to risk? That is the question. For a disabled person, it is a very important question.

It was one I had to deal with from the beginning. The beginning was the day I decided to live after suffering severe damage from a stroke. I couldn't sit, walk, talk, breathe, or eat. The only thing I could do was resolve to recover. How to do that?

The immediate answer was to undergo therapy. As I looked at the options, I found that each one presented a double-edged sword. On the one side was the safety issue. To learn to walk, I had to stand up. When I tried to stand up, I was afraid of falling down. I was afraid of breaking bones and having to deal with pain and treatment. On the other side, I knew that if I didn't try to stand up and walk, I never would move upright. I remembered the Chinese saying: A journey of a thousand miles begins with a single step.

I thought about love and thought about how risky it is to ask for love and to give it. Even to offer a hand in friendship provides an opportunity for rejection. But if we don't offer and give love, we truly won't get it. We do have to stick our necks out to receive the rewards. Life is a series of acts that "go for it." I know it is worth it.

I have learned that it is sometimes necessary to say no. The question becomes: how do I find the balance? I accept limitations. Acceptance does not mean defeat. It simply means knowing the bottom line and moving on. That bottom line can and does change. In the meantime, being aware of it is simply a way of minimizing risks.

As the writer Cynthia Heimel said: "When in doubt, make a fool of yourself. There is a microscopically thin line between being brilliantly creative and acting like the most gigantic idiot on earth. So what the hell, leap."

I have learned to accept all the help I can get so I can get out and keep going. I think of the helpers as being in two camps. One group deals with providing assistance to help me go on with living while I am disabled. Here we find people actively working to improve access to public facilities. It is important to have ramps to accommodate wheelchairs, walkers, scooters, and canes. The other group concentrates on rehabilitation. In addition to the therapies that are common, such as speech, occupational and physical, there is scientific research into re-growing nerve cells, for example, and an attempt to return the stroke survivor to pre-stroke status.

So we're always on the edge, so to speak. I maintain that recovery is still a reality. Notice I do not say it is a possibility. That is always a given. It is a reality, because advances are being made daily, and one day, as Christopher Reeve makes clear, we will benefit from these advances.

In the meantime, I remind myself that I never did like ferris wheels, roller coasters, or slash films. They scare me and give me nightmares, so I choose not to have those feelings.

Choice then becomes important. The ferris wheel and scary movies promise no improvement, so I choose not to do them. Horseback riding, swimming, and walking on a treadmill all promise recovery. I do these things because the potential payoff is so great. I don't think I am a hero because I do these things. I do them because I am helping myself.

I like to think of them as taking ordinary daily risks: Driving on a freeway, having children, buying stocks, entering a career, falling in love—all are risks. We call these calculated risks. The payoff, if we don't choose the risk?

We can become catatonic. We must play the juggling game. We must challenge our fears. In juggling, we tackle a ball, and not flaming spears. We choose within our abilities. Then we reach out a little bit more, a little further. I, for one, won't take up bungee jumping or dive out of an airplane, but I will continue to find things I can and will do. We can be what we want to be, but the important thing is to be! I have learned that I can feel the same amount of fear in not taking the risk, as I feel when I do take it.

Rousseau said it well: "Every man has the right to risk his own life in order to save it." Amen!

Change of Life

It wasn't male menopause! I know because I didn't have any symptoms. There was no perimenopausal period.

But what I did have was one heck of a change of life. And when life changes, so does one's life-style. One day I am active. I work as a psychologist and a teacher. I dance. I hike. I get around on my own. I am self-supporting, and I think, self-sustaining.

Late on the same day, I am a name on a hospital chart in the intensive care unit. I can't walk. I can't talk; I can't even breathe on my own. That's what the stroke did when it came. But I do not want to dwell on the recovery, which was slow, tedious, and sometimes painful. Recovery I had, but not to the point where my lifestyle could be the same. After seven years, I am still recovering and will do so until I die. But what I want to discuss is living. I think living means change and change means adapting to new styles of living. I think we do this when we are fully able-bodied, anyway. But when one becomes disabled, the change is a necessity. It is a given. We must change or die.

I listen when I hear wise things. I have treasured a quote from Norman Mailer, the American writer. He said, "there was that law of life, so cruel and so just, which demanded that one must grow or else pay more for remaining the same."

Taking stock after the stroke, I realized I did not have the mobility I once had, but I had the same drives and desires.

I was still the same person I was before the stroke. I liked fun and excitement. I kept busy so I would not be bored. I still loved teaching. I am, and always have been a ham, so I like getting up in front of people or reaching them in some way in order to help. I can help by educating them and being there as a friend. I can still listen to them. And I still can lecture and teach. So there you have it. In a nutshell. The talents one had before the disability are still there.

I have long been a member of a group called PRIMAL. It is an acronym for People Relating in Many Alternative Lifestyles. The suggestions of the title and of the group helped me take stock after the stroke and look forward to a future. "People" certainly included me, no matter what my physical disabilities might be.

Relating was still open. I like people and I like relating in every way. I like being with them and I like exchanging our energies, as well as our stories. The words in many alternative lifestyles underlined the cue. There is no one way to live a life. In a free country, I can design my own way.

There may be physical limitations, but the creative force is the same. In my case, I couldn't dance anymore, or hike. But I found a horse that provides me with motion and even dance steps. I don't hike, but my scooter lets me accompany my loved ones on their walks.

I say we have choices in this matter of lifestyle. We grow when we choose to change and to live life fully. I have always been a sensual person. I have always enjoyed sex. I continue in that way. While sexual activity has limitations, it still has activity. Paying attention to physical expression of love is heightened, as is the pleasure. When we accept the disability, we do not admit defeat. Instead we start to create that new lifestyle.

Where before we were intent on making a living, now we can make a life. The up side is that now we have more free time. We have time to reflect, to meditate, to dream, and to create. We adjust. We keep what still fits and discard that which we cannot use. I can go to the opera and to the

Shakespeare festival. Those are just two of my passions that I still indulge. I don't drive, but I can find drivers and so I get out. These are not compromises with life but are adjustments to reality that allow us to go on living.

So when lifestyles change, remember, it is not a change of your "style" but only a change in the way you express that style. It is new way of living!

The old song said it well: "There'll be some changes made today. There'll be a change in the weather and a change in the sea … from now on there'll be a change in me!" Go for it!

Section II: Therapy

The longest journey starts with a single step.

—ANON.

Key concept in stroke rehabilitation: You cannot superimpose normal function on abnormal muscle tone.

—BERTHA BOBATH

Tom walking with cane and caregiver Katie Mannix (top)
Tom at West Valley College "Adaptive" gym with Director Joan Worley
and P.T. Aide Roberta Wright

Disabled Lab Rat Serves Science and Self

What is a lab rat? Well, a lab rat is the subject of a serious scientific study performed in a scrupulously rigorous manner. That's the formal meaning. I also define it as a verb. The action is having fun and getting better and better.

My particular studies took place at the Veterans Affairs facility in Palo Alto, California. Funded by the federal government, the program is part of ongoing research and development. The study's chief investigator, David A. Brown, Ph.D., has a doctorate in exercise science and is also a physical therapist. The Palo Alto VA is one of only five centers in the country where varied disciplines interact in rehab-engineering studies. This means Dr. Brown works with engineers, including biomechanical experts. The group also has access to graduate students and faculty from nearby Stanford University.

I joined Dr. Brown's study about four years ago, when I was not as nimble or agile as I am now. The work he proposed to do with me was daunting. It frightened me! I did it anyway, because my motto through all my travail had been to try anything if it seemed it might help.

I am a stroke survivor, having had a cardiovascular accident more than five years ago. After a pessimistic prognosis by my doctors, I picked myself up, said "no" to their pessimism and looked around for therapy. My doctors did not have the answers and did not seem willing to look for them.

My therapists thought differently. They welcomed me and gave me the chance to work for improvement. I tried everything: swimming, adaptive physical education, horseback riding, speech and occupational therapy. I still participate in these activities on a daily basis. The results have been rewarding. I went from being strapped in my wheelchair and using an alphabet card to communicate, to where I am today. I sit straight, ride a horse, swim, and walk a little. I have resumed my career as a teacher, lecturer, and writer, not only in my professional capacity as a psychologist/sexologist, but also in dealing with disabled people.

Over the last four years I have participated in several different projects. While I call myself a "lab rat," they call me a "volunteer" or "participant." We do biofeedback. I say "we" because we work this magic together.

Dr. Brown's study views the pedaling of a bicycle as a paradigm for understanding leg movements, especially as they are related to locomotion. He and his colleagues created a bicycle-like device called an ergometer. The hypothesis is that it is possible to measure specific movement defects related to walking. It is also possible that using the ergometer will improve a patient's walking. In other words, the exercise can be useful in evaluation as well as treatment.

When I started in the study I rode a machine that resembled a bicycle. I describe it as a Rube Goldberg device. They strapped me onto the machine. They tied my legs into the pedals, and they told me to watch the video monitor while I pedaled. Easy for them to say! What I watched on the monitor were parallel lines. Each line represented the force of each leg as I pedaled. The object was to get the lines to come together. The effect was to equalize the amount of force, or energy output, of my two legs. It was not easy. It took a long time.

I could not understand how I could look at a video screen and make my legs behave as ordered. In some circles, they call that biofeedback. Dr. Brown calls it performance feedback. No matter what they call it, it was hard, but it happened. The progress was extraordinary. I tried many different body orientations, from almost prone to sitting upright. I pedaled backward and I pedaled forward. It worked!

Evaluation teams came to look at me. At first, I was shy to have strangers watching. To my pleasure, I found I did better with them there. The ham in me likes an audience. The evaluators solicited my views and I related my experience. They told me it was valuable to hear not only from the researchers but from the participant as well.

Along the way, I also reported my feelings and sensations to Dr. Brown. He says it is helpful for the ergometer's user to comment on the process, so that the researcher can adjust or make changes in the settings if necessary.

I then went into another study. Again, they strap me onto the device, which looks like a massage table with bicycle-like pedals at one end. Once attached to it, I move my legs as though I am riding a bike standing. The rear of the table tilts as I move. I must keep that table in a vertical position as I pedal up and down. My right leg must do the same kind of work as my unaffected left leg. If my legs are uncoordinated, the table tilts horizontally. If I am coordinated, the table stays vertical. Talk about hard work! Again, I monitor my progress on a screen, which shows a needle, much like a speedometer on a car. As I work the pedals, I see the needle move as it measures the extent of the force of each leg. Our next step is to do the exercises without the scope. In other words, there is no visual feedback.

I cannot explain the effect of getting such feedback on my ability to perform. What I can say is that it does work, and I am grateful for it. I am learning that it also works when I cannot see my progress on the monitor. It seems like a miracle.

I am improving my performance on the biomechanical devices. What is more important, I am improving my ability to walk in the real world. I can climb a flight of stairs, using the rail or a cane and using both legs, rather than dragging the right one. When I started I was unable to do one revolution on the table-bicycle when tilted at 20 degrees. Within a year, I could do ten or more revolutions with the bike tilted at 37 degrees. At first I could barely support 40% of my weight on the machines. Now I support more than 70% of my body weight. I have increased my endurance. I do not tire as easily. I am more in control of my clonus, a form of muscular convulsion common after a stroke.

My latest experiment was on a treadmill. Using virtual reality equipment (wearing goggles,) I had to step over different impediments as they appeared on my screen. We started at a speed of .2 mile per hour, and eventually I could walk at one mile per hour. After mastering the ability to move my affected foot in proper timing to get over the obstacles, we went on to increase the speed of my walking on the treadmill. At the conclusion of the experiment, I was walking at a speed of 2 miles per hour for five minutes and one mile per hour for twenty minutes. After the treadmill exercise, I walked down the hall of the VA building. At first, it took me 100 steps to go the distance, and at the end I was making it in 25 steps, which was a normal pace. The result was that my balance improved, I trusted my affected leg more and did not count only on my unaffected side. I learned to recover when I stumbled, and my endurance improved. Another big gain was the improvement in my confidence that I could walk.

I am grateful to be part of these studies, not only because I have gained so much personally, but also because I can help others. The lab rats and the scientists are pushing the perimeters in research on cardiovascular accidents. The new studies on the horizon will use virtual reality and gravity reduction to assist persons who are unstable in walking. I am ready. I am proud to be a lab rat going into the twenty-first century!

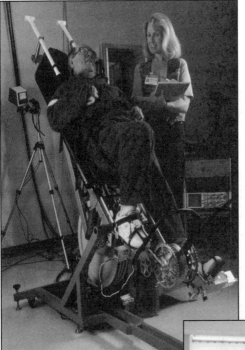

The "lab rat" performs on the
vertical bicycle while therapist
Cheryl Pierson takes notes.

Tom walks down the hall
at VA Research Center
with Dr. David Brown

Look Who's Talking! Me!

Coming out of my stroke I did not find many things funny. I laughed wryly, however, at the story of Tallulah Bankhead's volubility. After a session with her, one friend said he had just spent an hour talking with Tallulah for a few minutes.

I would have given anything to talk for a few minutes, an hour or a day or a year. I could not form the simplest word! It was the most distressing effect of the stroke. My right side was affected and I could not move without help. Somehow, terrible as that was, not being able to speak was worse. It terrified me.

Communication, after all, is how we get along in the world. I had been a teacher, and I talked. I liked to talk. It was my life's blood. Now it was taken from me. I could form words, sentences, and paragraphs in my head. I could not articulate them. The frustration was terrible. What was worse was knowing others could not understand me. I could not even tell my caregivers what I needed. After a while, I could use an alphabet card. I would point to the letters. The communications were, by necessity, short.

The reaction of caregivers, friends, even family, was strange and distressing. I felt they took my inability to communicate as a sign of incompetence. They treated me like a child or an idiot. They treated me as if I could not understand what was happening. As a result, they came and went, not seeing me at all. They invaded my privacy. They talked about other patients in my presence. They discussed my condition in front of me, without consulting me. I knew my mind was not affected. They acted as though it was. What to do?

I solved this particular problem by having a friendly nurse post a research paper I had written which served as notice that I was a highly educated person with several advance degrees. It was a reminder that just as one does not judge a book by its cover, one should not judge a person by the state of his body.

I had never considered the importance of spoken communication until I lost the power. My roommate in the rehabilitation facility was a quadriplegic who needed help with all body functions. What he did not need help with was his speech. His was a silver tongue. The women adored him. The nurses flocked to his side. They anticipated his needs and waited on him joyfully. Some even slept with him.

I look on Christopher Reeve with awe. My disability is not as severe, but I can relate to his experience. I admire his courage. I especially admire his speech. It is this ability that enables him to be such an effective advocate for disabled persons.

But there are others who are devastated by the loss of speech. This inability to communicate leads to anger and despair. One man I knew suffered a second stroke after making a good recovery in everything except his speech. His personality changed. He was angry all the time. He resigned himself to giving up life, and he began to die.

Today, after five years, I am able to speak well enough so I have resumed lecturing and teaching. I talk about my recovery and also about my professional field: sexuality and disability and aging. My voice is not what it was before the cerebral vascular accident (CVA), but I can communicate and I am understood.

The stages of the recovery were difficult. It took a long time, and it took five different therapists to help me get to where I am today. The lesson is hard to learn and hard to do, but it is important: Persevere! Never give up!

I had to get a new speech therapist when I moved to a

new city. She worked well with me until suddenly, without giving me any reason, she said I could no longer benefit from therapy. I did not agree and appealed to my HMO. I won that appeal and found a different speech therapist. She was the key to my making enormous advances. She was the first to suggest I might benefit from breathing therapy. I found a respiratory therapist and within weeks I had recovered most of my lost abilities. Her exercises included deep-breathing techniques to expand my lung capacity and usage. She prescribed using spoons from the freezer to massage my palate and throat. I tried it, and the therapy worked for me.

Although I am still self-conscious about my speech, I am able to lecture. I have appeared before stroke survivor groups, senior citizens, caregivers, and health professionals. I talk freely about my personal experiences, and use my professional knowledge to motivate people to keep trying, keep informed, enjoy their sexual lives, and to live fully each day.

It is important to remember how others react to us, and to educate them to our needs. We must tell them, and ourselves, that making hasty judgments about our abilities or our intelligence, based only on the way we look or sound, is not valid. It is important that other people see us as functioning human beings no matter what we look like or sound like. It is especially important to recognize ourselves in the same way! In this way, we maintain our integrity and help others do the same. In all events, it is important to salute Life!

Swim Therapy and How I Learned to Love It

To swim, or not to swim? Might as well ask, to be or not to be? It was a fundamental question when I began a long, arduous trek to recover from a stroke.

More than seven years ago, one of the things I liked to do very much, was to swim. Then, after the stroke, I couldn't swim, I couldn't walk, and I couldn't talk. I was getting physical therapy, but that wasn't enough. I needed something more, and I knew it.

My partner and I were living in Sacramento, California when I got out of the rehabilitation center. We heard about a water therapy program. We went to look at it. At the time I needed a gait belt and had trouble sitting straight in my wheelchair. It was daunting to think about getting into the water. How was I going to do it? The director of the program became my inspiration. She was a young woman who had spent three years in a wheelchair after an automobile accident. Told she would never walk again, she rebelled. She decided to swim. And swim she did. Therapy in the water not only got her walking, but today she skis and runs marathons. I believed her when she said I could do the same.

Well, I don't ski. I was never good at that anyway, and I don't run or even walk long distances, but I do so many things I couldn't do when I started.

So how did water therapy help me? My first teacher, along with the director Suzy, was John. John had also recovered from a stroke. He guided me in the pool. We actually walked in the water, and those were my first steps since the stroke. It felt very good. It was also the first time I really and truly believed that I could improve my condition if I worked at doing so. I began to know deep inside, that someday I would walk again.

We moved to San Jose where I enrolled in a new setting. I was in a class with four or five other recovering stroke patients. I needed my attendant to look after me. I was so afraid of aspirating water into my lungs that I almost gave up. My attendant had to hold me as I stretched and did some walking. The program was good for me, but I missed the one-on-one therapy that private lessons afforded.

Tom in the pool with swim therapist Gale

That is when I found a swim center in Palo Alto where I received private lessons. I liked the immediate feedback from the therapist. I got over my fear of aspirating and became bolder in the water. The therapist was there to correct my mistakes the minute I made them and to challenge me to a more daring performance.

I find that I do better with a teacher who is dedicated to watching me only, who pays attention not only to what I do but also to what I say, and who can encourage me to stretch to new heights of daring.

How far have I come? Well, I do a lot of other things too. I work out in adaptive physical education at a community college. I ride horses for "hippotherapy," I participate in experimental therapy at the Stanford Veterans Administration program, and I work with myself on an emotional and intellectual level as well. I mean that I also engage in meditative practices, and I read a lot and try to learn a lot. The various therapies complement one another, and, I think, provide a greater good than the mere sum of the parts might indicate.

Water therapy gave me my first feelings of hope. If I could walk in the water, then certainly someday I would walk on land. My self-confidence was boosted, and I was encouraged to try to do more. I now can walk in the water.

I now even can walk from the top of the stairs at the pool into the pool and then walk back out. What a feeling of accomplishment the first time I did that! I like the synergy, the exchange of energy between my dedicated therapist and me. It is best when there is an exchange of that energy, when we each have something to give the other. I can teach the therapist about what it's like to be the patient, and they teach me how to improve my performance.

So it is hard to say what water alone has done. But I do know this. The buoyancy afforded by the water makes it easier to move my affected limbs. The warmth of the water also induces comfort and even pleasure during the workout. I tried swimming in the college oudoor pool, but found the unheated water impossible to tolerate. In the warm water my clonus (muscular spasm) subsides, and I can do more. I am learning to swim again, even though my condition as a hemiplegic makes me lopsided. I have hope, and that keeps me coming back and keeps me improving. And oh, yes, did I mention it? It is also *fun*.

Perspectives On Rehab as a Person Who Survived a Stroke

I write here to share with you my experiences as a stroke survivor. Notice I did not say "patient" or "victim" or even "client." I am a survivor of a very serious stroke which hit me, unexpectedly, in 1991. I will not dwell on the "accident." (The medical establishment calls it a Cerebral Vascular Accident.) I almost died that day and again the next week when a second "accident" occurred.

But I didn't die. I got mad at my doctor when he asked if I wanted him to pull the plug! I decided I would live.

The road from almost total incapacity to what I am today, a man who can walk some, talk a lot, go to Shakespeare and Bach festivals, the opera, and jazz joints, was not easy. But I made it.

I had loving care in my home life, and this is the bottom line. My family and friends provided the crucial ingredient in caregiving: encouragement. I provided the determination. I had lost mobility, but I had not lost my ability to know what was happening and that I needed to do something about it.

Here's what I did then (and still do): I read about strokes. I went to lectures and support groups. I sought out people with similar experiences. I listened to many stories. I wanted to learn what to do so I could help myself, and maybe others as well. I went back to my doctoral disseration, which had been interrupted by the stroke. I finished it and got my Ph.D. My new career is still in teaching and writing and lecturing. But now I have added the subject of "Sexuality and Disability" to the previous one on "Sexuality and Aging."

Along with my studies, I do therapies:

I do "Adapted Physical Education" at a community college where I build my muscles, I stretch, and I socialize.

I swim at the YMCA. I also walk on water. I mean I walk in the water. It improves my confidence in my walking. Also, it feels good.

I ride a horse for therapy. They call it hippotherapy. This helps my pelvic area so I can support my torso better.

I am a "lab rat" in the Stanford-Veterans Administration program, where they do cutting edge research in stroke rehabilitation. I am in every study they can think of. I have ridden bicycles in all positions. I walk on a treadmill. Someday soon, I will be in a zero-gravity contraption, whatever that will mean.

I attended a community college program designed to teach stroke survivors new skills in mobility, occupational activity, speech, and memory.

I have had independent sessions with speech therapists. Many years after my stroke, and after at least one speech therapist said I would not improve, I had the good fortune to meet another therapist who suggested a new technique: using cold spoons on the palate. She found my soft palate had dropped. She also suggested I needed a breathing therapist, and between the two of them, my speech improved greatly.

In the first year after my stroke I had to learn to dress and to eat. Occupational therapists taught me how to use aids such as grab bars, to help my mobility.

The role of therapists and the use of adaptive devices are very important. Early in my treatment, I needed a leg brace. One of my doctors ordered a rigid brace. I needed a heavy shoe. It was so cumbersome I couldn't get my feet off the ground. Thankfully, a therapist knew enough to tell me to get rid of it. It was replaced with a plastic brace. It is important for therapists to know what the state-of- the-art is in devices. They must know what suits and is suitable for the client. Therapists should consult with the client. The client and the therapist are a team.

I have tried lots of other therapies; and some of them worked better than others, and some seemed not to work at all. For example, I did acupuncture for a while and qigong, which is an ancient Chinese exercise that stimulates the vital life energy flow along acupuncture meridians. These didn't do much for me. That is not to say they won't do much for others.

Now I am looking for new ways. I am hoping to drive again and am in the process of learning adaptive driving and getting the proper vehicle to do it. Of course, this will give me much more independence.

I think the bottom line, for therapists, is to start with helping motivate the client. I know this was most important for me. Since the day I refused my doctor's suggestion to "pull the plug," I have been strongly motivated to improve, to get better, to get on with my life.

Improvement can be slow, moderate, or fast. It can come as motivation to improve, to get better, to get on with my life. It can come in spurts of activity. It can come after a long period in which you have shown no improvement.

After all, the therapist knows that there may be plateau periods, and the client needs to take these into consideration. I think a better term than "plateau" is "silent growing," because I know that there is assimilation taking place. The key is to never give up.

Here's a story about never giving up. Six months after my stroke, my stroke doctor said I would never get any better. She said I had gone as far as I could. Mind you, I was still bent over in my wheelchair, couldn't walk, could hardly talk. When we asked why she said that the doctor replied, six months was the cut-off period; the medical literature said that if there wasn't improvement after six months, none would happen. Well, I tell you, I was devastated. My partner and I went home in despair. That lasted three days and then we got mad, mad enough to file a formal appeal with our HMO and demand continued therapy and a new doctor. We wrote about how the prognosis could be a self-fulfilling prophecy, and that, in fact, the doctor was wrong. We had learned of too many instances where improvement kept happening years after the event. Well, we won! Even the doctor apologized, and we became a strong working team after that. (See Appendix)

As for me, after all these years, I still make progress. Only recently, I found I had gained enough strength in my muscles and more ability to balance myself, that I was able to take myself into a tight toilet space. I no longer need assistance with getting in, sitting down, getting up, and getting out. A small deed for some, a big step forward for me. What I also built up, as I got stronger, was my self-confidence. We need the mental and emotional ability to go forward and take a risk.

Another and important need is sometimes overlooked: rehabilitation is a time of soul-searching for the clients. And it is a time for the therapist to address some very hard questions: Do the clients really want to get better? Are they willing to accept that the accident happened to them? Can they accept the limitations and yet accept the idea that the sky is the limit in overcoming those limitations? Recovery is possible. That thought must be kept in mind even when there are days when everything goes wrong. And on the other hand, the therapist may have to face the fact that some people give up. The time and energy spent may end up with heartbreaking results. Nobody said it would be easy!

Another word for this is "attitude." At present my own attitude is pretty positive. Yet there were times, and there still are times when I am impatient, depressed, sad, lonely, even hopeless. In these times I try to remember how far I have come. I am grateful that I learned to meditate before my stroke. It works miracles now, and I generally start my day with a meditation. It is then that I regroup, get my thoughts in order, and remain hopeful.

I lost a lot with the stroke, and I am learning to overcome the disadvantages. The biggest loss to me was not being able to speak. After all, I was a teacher, and communication was very important to me. I also was a painter, and now I can't hold a brush. I am right-handed, and it is my right side that is affected. Those losses weighed heavily on me.

But even there I found ways out, through, and around. I have learned the computer, having been taught how to use only my left hand for the typing. I can now write articles by myself. I have a graphics program so I can "paint" again. I communicate with the world through e-mail and I surf the net for new ideas and new friends. I even "talked" with Hillary Clinton's secretary one day.

I have been writing as though "I" did all these things by myself. That is not true. Without the team of therapists working with me, it probably would not have happened.

The key to rehabilitation, I think, is for the therapist and client to be a team. Together, we can meet the challenge. It must be wonderful for the therapist to see progress in her client. I know when I can help somebody else, I don't have time to feel sorry for myself. And we must remember not to curse the darkness, but to keep lighting the candles of hope and improvement, and remember that even the failures are steps to recovery. Thomas Edison was asked how it felt to have a thousand failures, which he did, before he finally perfected the light bulb. He replied, "I didn't have a thousand failures. I found a thousand different ways not to make the light bulb." So each happening is just another step on the way to recovery. And the one that didn't work, well, that's a learning also—an important learning—patience. When things aren't going right, look at the situation as a chance to try another way. It's the challenge that makes it exciting. The end goal is a better and more satisfying life.

Tom with hippotherapy group.
Front row: Tom and Chris, his assistant.
Back row: "Dudley," Barbara Heine and staff: Ann, Katie, and Susan.

Who's Afraid
of the Big Bad Horse

F ear was not the word to describe how I felt about horses eight years ago. Terrified is a more accurate description. However, I was more afraid of the effects of the stroke and determined to try anything to help me recover. Even a program which utilizes a horse and its natural movements as a therapy tool (hippotherapy!)

Gritting my teeth, I went. Do not ask how I got on the horse the first time. I choose not to remember. What I do remember and what I am here to tell you is that I have gone from hanging on to the horse for dear life to standing up in the saddle, while the horse moved. At first I mounted from the side. Now a hoist drops me on the horse.

At the Woodside, California, National Center for Equine Facilitated Therapy (NCEFT), I have ridden bareback, saddled, facing front and facing back. I go up hills and I go down hills. My horse and I jump small hurdles, and we also cover longer distances while I throw hoops onto a stick.

Has this therapy helped my recovery? You bet it has. I sit straighter and taller. I have more strength in my pelvic area, my back, my legs and my arms, even my right arm, which is the affected side.

I watched the Olympic equestrian competition between the USA and Australia with divided loyalties. Do I root for the home team or for my wonderful friends, therapists, and teachers—the Aussies—at NCEFT? I did both! After all, there are representatives from both countries at NCEFT. There are Barbara, Katie, Don, Ann, Jean, and Summer, to name but a few.

These are the people who inspire and give me courage to go forward. With their help and encouragement, I have gone from being a "fraidy cat" to being a total "ham." I love it. My horse Dudley and I love the audience. We show off for them and for our teachers. I am totally "in the moment" when I am on Dudley. It's a glorious feeling. Dudley and I complete our bonding when I feed him his carrots at the end of our session.

In the three years I have been riding I have gained much that shows physically. Even more important is what I have gained emotionally. I know that if I can ride a horse and do what I do on that horse, I can do anything!

Healing Through Empowerment

By Sharon Janus, Editor

The Magic of Horses. Horses as Healers.

Ralph Waldo Emerson, in his essay "Heroism," wrote "The characteristic of heroism is its persistency." Dr. Tom Matola has tested and lived the truth of this statement since 1991 when he suffered a debilitating stroke which left him unable to talk and unable to use the right side of his body. Tom was angry. He felt that his body had betrayed him, and admits that he lost much of his courage because of the stroke. He went through conventional rehabilitation and he improved. However, it was only after participating in therapeutic riding that Tom found his courage again.

It wasn't easy for Tom to decide to ride. He and his wife, Roberta Johnson, a retired judge, knew of the positive effects of hippotherapy, using the horse as a therapist. Their sister-in-law, Ann Kulchin, is the founder and director of B.O.K. Ranch, a therapeutic riding center located in Los Altos Hills, California. Tom and Roberta had visited B.O.K. on many occasions and witnessed the progress made by children with cerebral palsy. Yet, Tom was scared of horses.

Prior to his stroke, Tom had been on a horse only once and it wasn't a great experience. The animal, an ex-racing horse, decided that they were going to go for a dip in the ocean. Tom disagreed, but she won the argument. The experience terrified Tom and left him with bitter memories. Tom was understandably resistant to the idea of riding—therapeutic or not.

Roberta and Ann, however, knew full well that the effects of Tom's stroke could be lessened with the help of horses, so they kept talking to him. It didn't take long for the talking to work. Tom soon realized that he had to ride. He understood that he wouldn't get better unless he helped himself and he yearned to improve.

Determined to progress physically, Tom told himself, "I'm going to turn this around." He began riding at B.O.K. Ranch.

After a time, Ann suggested that he move to the National Center for Equine Facilitated Therapy in Woodside, California. This center was better equipped to help Tom. Bob Heine, the director, even put in a hoist to make it easier for Tom to mount his horse.

When asked whether or not riding has improved his condition, Tom responds, "Absolutely." He is talking again and his pelvic region has become stronger, and his posture has improved. Tom also has more strength in his arms.

Though he isn't walking yet, he can and does stand in the saddle strengthening his legs and preparing to take his next steps. Tom has every intention of not only walking again, but of getting back into Tango competition. In fact, several years ago he won a Tango championship.

Tom has been riding Dudley at the National Center for about two years. He believes that Dudley will help him reach his goal of dancing again; he also believes that one of Dudley's greatest gifts is his energy. "Horses have a lot of energy. I can feel it." Tom adds, "It's all transferred."

Tom also believes that riding presents a chance for a person to experience a oneness with another creature. He is quick to point out that eastern religions teach that this experience is the source of spiritual enlightenment. Besides feeling a oneness of unity, Tom says that riding also teaches a person to be present in the moment. "Every moment that I am on a horse, I must feel and trust that horse," he states. "In essence, we blend our energies." After talking with Tom, a person is left with the feeling that for him riding Dudley is much more than sitting on top.

Besides helping Tom experience ancient insights into religion and philosophy, Dudley has also helped him grow psychologically. He has regained confidence in himself and in his abilities. Dudley empowers him. "If I can get on a horse, I can do anything," Tom laughs.

Tom's attitude reflects in other areas of his life. He can indeed do anything—and he does. Roberta reports that Tom's schedule keeps him out and about six to eight hours a day! He has much to keep himself busy. Tom is a writer and has published many articles in both scholarly and mainstream journals. Since the stroke still affects Tom's right hand, he taught himself to use the computer keyboard with his left hand. When he's not writing, Tom will often visit hospitals and rehabilitation centers where he helps others cope with the effects of strokes.

In an article entitled, "You Must Maintain Hope After a Stroke," Tom writes, "My mission in life is to continue as a teacher." Tom is certainly dedicated to his calling. He not only shares his knowledge and experience with others who have suffered from strokes, he inspires them and urges them to have faith and hope. Tom teaches that without hope, a person's psyche and spirit wither away. He believes these effects are as bad—if not worse—than the physical effects from an illness.

Tom teaches priceless lessons using more than words. He is a living, breathing, flesh and blood inspiration to others. Riding has opened his mind and given him countless new avenues to explore. Practicing what he preaches, Tom finished his doctoral dissertation after his stroke and received his Ph.D. in Sexology.

Courage? Persistence? Tom lives it. What's best is that

he shares it with others, empowering them as he has been empowered. As the saying goes, "What goes around comes around."

Tom preparing to mount the horse with NCEFT staff and volunteers

Dancing Horses and Me

Once upon a time, before my stroke in 1991, I won a dance contest. I was very good and very proud of my prowess as a tango master!

Once upon a time, years after my stroke, I could barely walk and had resigned myself to dreaming of dancing. Then I met Java! I wish I could say it was love at first sight! It wasn't. Java was just the fourth in a series of horses I had been riding since I began hippotherapy several years ago. Considering I was and still am scared to death of horses. I have always felt a certain elation after each lesson. After all I was still alive. I have become so much stronger and better for the weekly "rides."

To understand the marvel of Java, you have to know her predecessors. My first mount was Shane whom I met at the B.O.K.(sic) in Happy Valley, California. The B.O.K. is run by my companion's family. I knew about the wonderful work they were doing with young people, those who were autistic, had cerebral palsy, multiple sclerosis, or other disabling conditions.

Then it was my turn. I started at B.O.K. I was one of the few adults in the program. Shane was a beautiful quarter horse, big and gentle. The volunteer working with me was also big and gentle. Charles would help lift me onto the horse from my wheelchair that was on a raised platform. This was scary because sometimes Shane moved and I feared I would slip to the ground. At first I held onto Shane's mane, and I bent forward, hanging on for dear life. I had only been on a horse once before in my life and then it had run away with me. I was terrified. I said "giddyap" when I wanted to stop, and I said "whoa" when I wanted to go. I finally got it right, but I always wondered why I needed this. It felt like torture. It is a long way off the ground from the top of a 15 hand horse. But the wonderful folks at B.O.K. knew better than I did. With their encouragement, I kept going back week after week.

After a while, I was jumping small hurdles, going cross country, touching my head as I rode and throwing and catching balls and hoops—no small achievement for me, who had only the use of his left arm. Most of all, I knew my posture had improved and so had my torso strength.

After a year, the B.O.K. referred me to the National Center for Equestrian Facilitated Therapy in Woodside, California for therapy. Barbara Heine, a leader in the hippotherapy community, is a licensed physical therapist. She and her staff first evaluated me to see if I was a fitting candidate for the rigorous program they conducted. I was lucky. I was accepted.

At the B.O.K., I held the reins and guided the horse. At NCEFT, a therapist holds the reins and walks behind the horse. At B.O.K., I transferred from my wheelchair directly to the horse. At NCEFT, a hoist lifts me onto the horse.

My first ride was on Dudley. He was the biggest horse I had ever seen. It was only because I knew he was specially trained for the work that I was able to make myself get on him. Barbara and her staff put up even more challenges.

I rode bareback. I rode backward and it was all I could do not to grab Dudley's tail. I rode on an English saddle; no longer did I have the horn of a western saddle to help. Scared or not, the therapy did wonders for my posture, balance, and self-esteem.

I had to stand up in the saddle, first when Dudley was at rest, and later when we were in motion. Just as Dudley and I bonded and I felt more comfortable, he was retired from active service.

Next came Odie, who was likable enough but not very smart. Like Garfield's canine companion, he was a sloppy eater, had the bad habit of holding his head down so I tipped forward, and he was stubborn in those ways. Nevertheless, we persevered together. Odie made Dudley look skinny because Odie was huge, broad, and tall. I couldn't wear my leg brace on Odie because he was so broad.

Odie and I parted company after the day he tried to roll with me in the sand. He went right, and I started to slip off to the left. Thankfully my therapists walking with me grabbed me so I wasn't thrown. Somehow, though, Barbara talked me into continuing. My heart was no longer in it. I trusted my handlers enough to go on. I didn't trust Odie any more.

Not long after that Odie left and Java came into my life. Java is a black beauty, a thoroughbred. She is proud and slick. She eats delicately. When she walks, she prances. In fact, she dances! Barbara, one day, asked if I would like to see Java tango. Of course, I said, thinking she would dance with Java. But no, that was not to be. I was Java's partner as she cued Java to begin the tantalizing steps of the Argentinean dance. What a thrill! I wanted more and more I got. Java not only tangos, she can do the samba and rumba as well.

As much as this sounds like fun and games for us, it is serious therapy. Barbara can explain it in scientific terms. I can only say that the increased motions, sidestepping, twisting and turning to the musical rhythms, are improving my posture and strengthening all my muscles, especially those on my sides.

I have a confession to make. I am a ham. I had a short amateur career in drama and loved the attention. After all, that is what I got when I was a teacher, too. I feel I perform better with an audience. So I have a vision. Java and I are starring in a show. Of course it has to be in an arena, not on a stage. We dance to the music of a really big orchestra. The audience goes wild. The applause is deafening as we take bow after bow. When we finish the last encore I have another vision, and this time my dancing partner is my real life partner.

"Tally Ho" at NCEFT

Two Views of Hippotherapy

By Thomas Matola Ph.D. and Barbara Heine

The client, Tom Matola, speaks:
Have I got a dancing partner! She is a real lady. She knows how to behave. You could truthfully call her a thoroughbred. She does not have four left feet, but she does have four feet. She is my therapy horse. Java is her name. She is a beauty and she is a cheap date.

Since my stroke seven years ago I have often dreamed that I was dancing. Once, before I lost the use of my right side, I did win a tango competition. I have had a good and beautiful dancing partner before, but this lady is tops. She carries me and she leads, or rather is led by Barbara, her proud owner and trainer. Oh, we make such beautiful music together.

I was telling Barbara about my dancing days and she said, okay, let's dance. Java, she said, can do the tango and the rumba too. I said, okay, show me. I prepared to watch from the sidelines. Instead the music started and there we were a perfect twosome, Java and I, doing the tango! Oh, joy! In her book "The Magic of Horses" Sharon Janus talked about my dancing and predicted I would tango again. She was right. What is it they say? Never ask for something because you do not know in what form it will come. Who would have dreamed I would realize my dream with a thoroughbred horse? I am happy. My partner is happy. Together we make a mean looking couple. We look good and we feel good.

I started riding for therapy five years ago. I was afraid of horses then and am still afraid of them. I also have learned to trust them and the trainers. Before Java I had made significant strides in my recovery. I sat up straighter. I had strong pelvic control. My legs moved better. My physical stamina had improved. My emotional state also benefited. I gained self-confidence.

What has the added factor of dancing done? Well, it is fun. In addition, I found I was working harder as Java side stepped to the strains of the tango. I needed to maintain good balance so I had to adjust my posture as she danced.

I am not sure I can explain all that is happening now. What I can do is state that I feel something good is happening. Maybe it is just more of what has been happening all along plus additional work. The side step motion of Java seems to be working on my side muscles more than the previous motions I used. Yes, I am still afraid of horses. Yes, I still look forward to going to class every week. I think I will bring not only carrots for Java, but a bouquet of roses for my lovely dancing partner.

∽

The therapist, Barbara Heine, speaks:

Something very special happened during a hippotherapy session recently, and because it reminds me of why I am so passionate about hippotherapy, I would like to share it with you. It involves a patient Tom, a little brown mare called Java, and a great team of people.

First a little background—Tom is a delightfully irreverent 67 year old stroke survivor. Initially, Tom's prognosis was dismal and he fought many bitter battles with various branches of the medical profession to continue therapy services. It was this tenacity that led him to seek out hippotherapy. There was only one problem—Tom was terrified of being on a horse!

During Tom's initial evaluation we carefully looked at and discussed the relevant issues. Tom weighed 170 pounds and spent the majority of his day in a wheelchair, resulting in an extremely kyphotic sitting posture that was definitely his "well of stability." Apart from his anxiety, weight, and lack of mobility, there were no contraindications or precautions to preclude hippotherapy as a viable option for him. I assured him that we had a suitable horse and our staff and horses were expertly trained to guarantee safe mounting and dismounting. Together we agreed to take on the challenge and so began a journey that has spanned almost five years.

After several months, we began to see changes, albeit small ones, in trunk strength and trunk/pelvic dissociation in the sagittal plane, but disappointingly very little overall improvement in sitting posture. Then came the first setback. The horse we had always used for Tom, a weight carrying Quarterhorse called Dudley, was not aging well and had to be retired. We had to come up with another horse or discontinue treatment.

Since Tom's weight is a significant factor, it seemed the obvious choice was the only breed specific weight carrying horse in our barn—Odie. Odie is a 12 year old Haflinger with the face of an angel, the mind of a hyperactive 2 year old and the body of a fully loaded Mack truck. He is a relative newcomer and although totally bomb proof, his distractibility is still not completely resolved. Since final horse decisions are mine, I tossed the whole thing around in my mind for a bit longer. On the plus side—totally reliable, and certainly able to carry Tom's 170 pounds with ease. On the minus side—distractible, leading to losses of rhythm (which Tom's anxiety radar would pick up on!), a little on the broad side, and a choppy walk that did not produce significant perturbations in the frontal or transverse planes. The deciding factors were that he was safe and Tom could continue treatment.

Tom made the transition, full of trepidation of course, but he gradually settled down. As anticipated, Odie's movement did not challenge Tom in the frontal and transverse planes, nor did it provide facilitation of trunk rotation and pelvic weight shifts. After several months, Tom had reverted to his "stuck" preferred sitting position and he seemed less motivated. We were trying to come up with treatment options to address these problems when Odie developed a foot abscess. Back to the drawing board—did we have another horse that could carry Tom?

Enter Java, a plain, brown Thoroughbred/Quarterhorse mare 15.1 hands high. We first got Java three years ago and although she has a spectacular walk, she has a major conformation fault. Her head and neck are set too low onto her shoulders making her very heavy on the forehand. Her temperament and movement were too good not to take her into the program, but we had to address the issue of her confirmation and the absence of a top line. Over the next three years Java was consistently ridden and long lined to build a strong top line along the length of her body. We basically changed her shape to enable her to "carry herself." The result is a horse that has strong musculature to support her back, self carriage under saddle, and the ability to perform second level dressage movements. She would be perfect for Tom! As an added precaution we placed a vaulting gel pad under the saddle to evenly distribute and absorb Tom's weight.

Making yet another horse transition was traumatic for Tom, but his "team" (we always have the same tall sidewalkers for Tom as the familiarity helps keep his anxiety down) was so supportive and calm that even he had to admit that he was being silly to be so nervous. Java didn't let us down—after a rock solid mount and 15 minutes of a rhythmical walk that was as smooth as silk, Tom was chatting away, without a care in the world, his motivation back to normal.

About 15 minutes into the second session, I increased the tempo very slightly (I was long lining). The therapist and I became very excited as we saw, for the first time, increased trunk rotation, trunk/pelvic dissociation in the frontal and transverse planes, and pelvic weight shifts. At that moment, I heard Tom tell one of his sidewalkers how he misses not being able to dance. I have always associated dressage with dancing so I immediately picked up on Tom's comment and told him that Java can dance and would he like to see what it feels like.

There was a good natured snort of derision, which since I know Tom so well I totally ignored, and as we passed the next corner, I prepared to turn down the center line. Tom was still prattling on about "dancing horses my foot!" when this wonderful little mare carefully leg yielded four steps left, then four steps right, and so on down half the center line. On the first leg yield, Tom yelled "Whoa" as his trunk leaned precariously left but before he had time to worry, she was leg yielding right and he had straightened up. The second leg yield left produced much less of a gravitational postural response and by the third and last, his trunk remained centered (a wonderful example of adaptability). His "Whoa" had been replaced by "Wow" and as we proceeded on a straight line, Tom was ecstatic and his fears had been replaced by an entirely new sensation—excitement.

We did the exercise twice more and the therapist and I watched in rapt attention as we saw consistent symmetrical weight shifting and trunk co-contraction in all planes as his body accommodated not only to the lateral movement, but also the acceleration and deceleration as each leg yield changed direction. The whole team was ecstatic, even Java seemed to know she'd done well. Tom was thrilled because he was "dancing" again and we simply couldn't believe that we had finally found the way to get Tom out of his slumped fixture posture—his well of stability. We have since added the shoulder in and Tom now proudly reports that he can do the tango and the rumba. As he so succinctly puts it—he's dancing again—with his horse!

Hippotherapy is wonderful and what we have accomplished with Tom makes me feel good. However, it also reminds me of the responsibility that we all have, to our professions, our patients, and the horses that we use. Simply using a horse is not good hippotherapy. We must constantly ask ourselves: are the patient's responses appropriate to the functional goals of the treatment plan, is the treatment safe, is the horse sufficiently trained and conditioned not merely to do the work but to provide the movement quality and variety needed to address the patient's needs? It is not only research, but constant problem solving and striving for excellence in ourselves and our horses, that will ensure that hippotherapy assumes its rightful place within the professional health community as an accepted therapeutic intervention.

Horseback Riding as Sex Therapy

A recent innovation in therapy for various physical and emotional disabilities is the use of horses. About a year after suffering a severe stroke, I started "hippotherapy." In the years since that time, I have been rewarded with a healthier body. My head, neck, back, pelvis, and arms are stronger and more flexible.

Although I hadn't expected it, I also found my emotional and psychological health greatly improved. A sense of well-being accompanied the exercise.

What came as a bigger surprise was an improvement in my sexual life. I am a sexologist by training. I know that "how-to-do-it" sex manuals stress the importance of strengthening the pelvic area to achieve greater sexual satisfaction for yourself and your partner. Riding a horse is an excellent exercise to this end. In order to stay on a horse, one must sit properly and move the pelvis in rhythm with the horse's three-dimensional motion. The better the rhythm is maintained, the better the ride. The more one rides, the more one's endurance improves. The same can be said for the sex act.

It is basic, in sex, to be "in the moment." It is joyful to act in concert with your partner, without thinking, but just being in the act. To ride a horse is to experience a "oneness" with another creature. As a matter of fact, if I am not completely aware of every movement of my horse, I will fall off. Eastern religious disciplines teach this principle. I know it works in daily living, in exercise, and in sex.

Because I must be present in the moment, every moment I am on that horse, I must feel and trust the horse. We blend our energies. What I cannot provide because of my handicap, the horse supplies. I became aware of this phenomenon when I first watched handicapped children ride. Those with cerebral palsy, for example, couldn't walk on their own, but sat tall and "walked" as the horse walked. Such a sight is inspirational and educational. As I watched those children blend their energy with their mounts, I found the confidence I needed to go on with my quest for improvement.

As I continue to improve my skills on the horse, I also continue to improve my well-being, including the important sensual relationships. Sex is better. I become stronger physically. I live more in the moment, savoring what each sense brings me: the taste of food and wine, the smell of the earth, the touch of my grandson, the sound of a friend's voice on the telephone, and the totality of sensations in lovemaking.

Section III: Sexy Stuff

Love One Another,
But make not bond
Of love.
Let it rather be a moving sea
Between the shores of your souls.

—KHAHIL GIBRON

Adam and Eve Romp in the Back Garden

Hooray for Sex,
an Equal Opportunity Pleasure

In the beginning there was Sex. Of course there was. How else did Adam and Eve beget Cain and Abel? I tell you this to cite authority for my proposition that sex is okay! I always accepted this word as gospel. That is, I did until I had a stroke.

When I finally decided I was going to survive, I started thinking about living my life fully. I started thinking, not only about how to get around in a chair, but I started thinking about sex. I am by profession a psychologist with a major in human sexuality. I call myself a sexologist. But I did not know about the possibilities for sex with my new disability. So I started asking questions. I asked my doctors. They did not answer. Their "hems" and "haws" indicated, to me, that they did not know what to say, or certainly did not want to talk about it. I asked the nurses. They looked the other way. I am sure they had answers but did not want to discuss the subject. I knew they knew about persons with disabilities having sex, because I knew my roommate was having sex. He not only told me, but I could hear him and his partner. And he was a quadriplegic.

As a professional, I was not easily put off. I persisted and insisted on getting the subject of sex and disability out in the open. I chose to write and publish. My first post-stroke article was about sex and the disabled. The Canadian magazine *It's OKAY!* published it. I clipped the article, framed it, and hung it over my bed in the hospital. Now others knew that I knew sex was not only okay, but it was fun, inexpensive, and great exercise.

But spreading the word isn't easy. My friend, the sex educator Stan Dale, tried to get the California Department of Motor Vehicles to issue a custom license plate reading: SEX IS OK. Guess what? The Department of Motor Vehicles said it was obscene. Stan filed an appeal and after a hearing he won! So now we have a legal basis for asserting that sex is okay.

Having settled that, let's talk about what kind of sex? There are hundreds of books and articles published about sex. Most of the titles intend to titillate. Most of the information is sketchy. Following the "pop psychology" trend we now have "pop sexology." Like fast food, the books fill you up but leave you undernourished.

A modern sage said that everything in life is easier if you are having great sex! How to do this? I think my golden rule here is to use it or lose it.

Sex is healthy! You cannot beat the aerobic benefits. It is good for the heart, for the circulation. It gives you a rosy complexion. It jump-starts the day, better than coffee or a cigarette or whatever!

Take time for sex! That dynamite lady, Dr. Ruth, said that most sex events take less than fifteen minutes. Surely we each have that much time, no matter how busy our schedules are, each day or week or month. How much time? Whatever! "Quickees" or "Longees." Whatever you want. Dr. Ruth's timetable is not one set in stone. It is only an observation she made. When there is time, take your time. Enhance the setting. Turn on the music. Arrange the flowers. Don't forget the sweet talk. When there is not time, a "quickie" is more nourishing than no sex at all.

Make the time and place for sex! If you have to consider the kids, the grandparents, or even the neighbors, carve out the right private time. Somehow you can do it. "Quickies" are especially appropriate when private time is short. Day or Night? Or in between. Whenever, is my answer. Whenever the mutual mood strikes, whenever there is space, and wherever that space is, take advantage. A good night's sleep gives us appetite and energy for good-morning sex. Our imaginations are also fueled by good-night dreams.

Sex is playful! It is fun! Life is serious. So what? I say go for it. Being playful doesn't mean you can't be serious. It does mean you can enjoy the joy of it. Use toys and games, if you want. Read the literature. The Kama Sutra is a beautiful example of beautiful people loving each other.

Talk about it! The spoken word is powerful. The unspoken word can trap us. Do not be afraid to use sexual language. The debate over the use of the "F" word has been fought and now is in the realm of "free speech." A courageous former Surgeon General brought the "M" word to light, and the subject now can be addressed with understanding, instead of superstition. Masturbation will not put hair on your palm. It will, if you want, bring pleasure and not pain.

Be compassionate! When your partner is a loved one, you owe that person respect. Be open. Be honest. Know what you like and what you don't. Say so. Sex play is not a power trip. It is an expression of human bonding in most intimate terms.

Be creative! Position is not a matter of superiority and inferiority. It is a matter of mutual discovery. Religious injunctions may play a part here. But if they don't, then you can create the rules as you go along. And you can change the rules, if you want. Man on top, woman on top. Only you can say. Experiment with other coupling "ways and means." It is fun to explore. Position is especially important to persons with disabilities. Accommodations need to be made. Movements may call for assistance. Whatever the disability, there is a way to sexual play and fulfillment. Look for it. Find it.

Feed the Spirit! Yes, sex can be a spiritual experience. I have left my body and felt closer to the universe while having sex. And at the same time, I have felt completely within my body. To me, it is a holy union. Sex nurtures my body and my soul.

Hooray for sex! It really is an equal opportunity pleasure. As long as you don't scare the kids, the neighbors, or the horses, sex is okay anytime, anyplace, and anyhow. Especially for us disabled folk, we get by with the help of our loved ones. And loving is where it's at. Enjoy! Make it so!

The Disabled Are Better Lovers and I Should Know

The title is catchy, is it not? Well, I believe it. I should know! I claim two credentials in this field. One, I am a disabled person, having had a stroke seven years ago. Two, my professional discipline is the field of human sexuality. I am a "sexologist."

Maybe we, disabled persons, are better lovers because we try harder, but I think it is more than that. I think the law of compensation comes into play. As we lose one ability, we learn to develop and use others. For example, if one loses sight, the other senses are enhanced. One smells better, hears better, identifies things by touch better. The loss of a leg may result in increased ability of a remaining leg or of the arms. I know a woman who was born without arms. She has earned two doctorates, practices a profession, raises a family, drives a car, and does all of these things using her legs, her feet, her toes.

Disability can, and does, lead to great sex. As a disabled person, I must live "in the moment." I must always focus on my safety. I look before I do. Before I stand up to transfer, for example, I make sure to set my chair brakes. I am aware of the consequences of my acts.

In sex, being "in the moment" is of paramount importance. I am aware of my lover and her responses. The ancient arts of tantra, and other love forms portrayed in the Kama

Sutra, focus on slow-moving sensuality. It is a dance of love. Actions are slow and deliberate, as when I take the halting steps I am able to take with my disability. Nothing is automatic. I plan each step for optimum gain. In eating, I must choose each morsel carefully, chew deliberately, and swallow with full attention, or else I choke. I delight in a single raisin and learn that gulping giant mouthfuls make me miss the nuance of the flavor. So it is in sex. Each caress, each kiss, has my full attention.

In drinking wine, I find slow swirling in the glass, inhaling the aroma, taking small sips to distinguish the differing flavors adds to the enjoyment. So it is in sex. Each movement, each sigh, intensifies pleasure.

In slowing down the pace of my daily living, I find serenity in solitude, joy in listening to my friends talk, intellectual interest and amusement in watching birds fly and squirrels argue. I do not fly over the country any more. I drive, and I see things I never saw before. So it is in sex. Slowly attending to the senses of feeling, smelling, tasting, hearing, and seeing, I find ecstasy in the sexual coupling.

My disability left me with impaired mobility on the right side. I have learned to compensate. I am able to use only my left hand. So I learned to type, eat, wave, move my chair, shave, and care for myself with one hand. I cannot move my right side. So I learned to use my left.

It took time to learn these things. It took time to learn ways to compensate in lovemaking. My partner and I created ways. New positions were first. We earned an unforeseen dividend when we found we had to communicate for this purpose. We learned to speak more honestly and openly. So it is in sex.

Communication leads to communion in sexual congress. It is what makes it an act of love and not lust.

I feel the lessons learned as a result of my disability are lessons for the able-bodied as well. In a world without barriers, we are all equal. We are all humans first. We can all benefit by slowing down and smiling at the roses.

Sex and a Stroke:
Is There Sex After a Stroke?

Yes, Virginia, there definitely is. Yes, it may mean a new life style. Yes, it may mean a chance to show imagination and yes, it definitely means a chance to show more loving! If there was sex and love before the stroke, there will be sex and love after the stroke. There will be sexual desire after the stroke.

When I began my recovery, after the initial battle with just physical survival, I wondered about my future sex life, since this had always been important to me. Since I didn't get much help from the hospital staff, I decided to find out myself. Professionally, as a sex therapist, and personally, as a sexually active adult, I decided I would pursue my studies in the field of sexuality and disability. Prior to the stroke, I was engaged in getting my doctorate in sexology, with an emphasis on sexuality and aging. After my stroke, I changed that to an emphasis on sexuality and disability. When I started looking into the field of disability, I found very little had been written about sexuality and the disabled. In the four years since I started specializing, more has gotten into the literature, but I think not enough. So what have I found out?

One of the big questions is always: Is sex harmful? Does a stroke survivor get worse if they engage in sexual activity? In most cases, sex has the opposite effect. Sexual activity not only cheers up the individual, but it has good physical effect.

For one, it increases the pulse rate and can be considered an "aerobic" activity. It gives pleasure and thus adds to the zip of living.

Of course, if one was not interested in sex, or really enjoying it before the stroke, chances are that will not change. And since sex is a personal preference, then that is perfectly okay, too.

And of course, sex may be difficult at times. Just surviving may be the most important factor, so sex naturally goes on the back burner. And there are obstacles to overcome. Is it worth it?

While it is pleasurable in most cases, and it is a part of being alive, it may not be as important as being able to breathe.

But when the desire and interest are present, what to do? I think it is important, in the face of a physical disability, to always remember that the major sex organ is the brain.

Thinking about sexual pleasure fuels desire and libido. It is here that an attitude of tender loving care, TLC, is born. It is here that fantasy has its origin. It is here that creativity is born. And it is here that we recognize we are living in the moment.

It is here we need to communicate our thoughts. It is important to make our desires known to our partner and, equally important, to listen to our partner's expressed wishes.

When I think about communication, I remember two friends, each of whom was severely disabled. Both were quadriplegic. One could use only his head and one finger. The other needed help with everything except feeding himself. But, oh, how they could communicate. They loved life and themselves and others. And they let others know that a silver tongue was their way to the world, and I never met anybody who wasn't completely charmed by them. And each attracted extremely attractive sex partners.

I also remember my own situation. Right after the stroke, I could not talk or write. I was using an alphabet card. Life was dark for me then, and I think one of the hardest parts was not being able to make myself and my feelings and needs known to others. Needless to say, I worked very hard to get my speech back. I am still working on getting better.

Once you have established a form of communication, you can focus on the physical aspects of your sexual experience. It is important, in this regard, to check out the system. If, before the stroke, you experienced physical problems, they will probably still be there. Even if there were no physical difficulties before, it is a good idea to have a medical examination by a gynecologist or a urologist. Often there is therapy that can help.

It may also be that medications are affecting your sexual performance. This may be especially true if you experienced no problems before but are having problems since. In that case, your doctor can check it out for you.

With all of us, men and women, the effect of drugs may cause problems. For example, drug taking may make one relax too much. The medical exam is therefore important. There are also sex therapists who are skilled in dealing with these problems.

For males there is a simple test, as we men naturally get an erection each night. Use the "roll of stamps" test. That is, put a roll of stamps around the penis. In the morning you will know you had an erection! The perforations on that roll of stamps will be broken.

While the genital areas are important, equally of value in sexual activity is the whole body, and especially the skin. This is a vast playground. The sense of touch is exciting and it feels good to be touched and to touch another. There are many nerve endings in the skin, which give pleasure. Explore your own sensations, and find out from your partner what feels good to her or him. And speaking of sensations, explore also the smells, tastes, sights, and sounds that give sensual pleasure.

I would like to stress that, like any activity, sex is most enjoyable, and done best, when all attention is centered on the activity. Also important is the attitude. While the physical and emotional outcome is valuable, I think it important not to lose sight of the fact that it is the warmth and loving feelings that do us the most good. And let's not forget that it is just plain FUN.

Recently I attended a lecture by Dr. Ruth. She had to stand on two boxes to be seen above the podium. So there she was, all four-feet-something of her, but to look at her you felt she was at least ten-feet tall. That is the way she acted.

So what did she say first of all? She said: Sex is not just about procreation, but it is also recreation. For those of us old enough to be coming to this senior center, enough said about procreation. Let's focus on the recreation part. The fun part.

Since a stroke makes us hemiplegic, we know one or the other side is affected. Is this a problem? Or a challenge? In most cases the equipment is not affected, but the way we play may require some changes or adaptations.

Once the mood is set, we can make the necessary adjustments. This includes finding the right positions. With one partner affected, there may have to be a change in who is on top. So, consider the options: side by side, scissors, sitting in a chair with the unaffected partner on top.

Often cited as a problem is dryness of the vaginal area. Easily corrected: use a vaginal gel or consider oral sex.

Also important to remember is that penis-vagina, or PV, intercourse is not the only sex play there is. Sometimes caresses are enough.

Ask this question: "Are both partners happy with what is happening?" The key to this question is communication, the open, honest communication between the partners. Make time for this loving relationship. Talk about it, too. And always remember to take your time. After all, what is the rush?

Aging, Sexuality, and Disability or How I Learned to Live with All Three

The great baseball player Satchel Paige asked, "How old would you be if you didn't know how old you were?" I like that. I agree that age is a number, but I also know that at my age I am aging.

The great mystery writer Agatha Christie said her husband, the archeologist Max Mallowan, got more interested in her the older she became. I like that. I agree. I think I am aging in an interesting way.

The great poets of the ages have agreed that love and sex makes the world go around. I certainly agree.

And I, who am aging and disabled after a stroke, say that we disabled people make better lovers. Our aging provided the experience and our disability taught us patience and the meaning of love and caring by and for others.

It took a while for me to fashion this creed for myself. There is so much propaganda out in the world, all of it saying that only the young matter. Only those who are perfect by an advertising standard can have fun or fulfillment. By looking around me, however, I saw that was not true. My older friends were having fun and living well. Many of my friends, younger or older, who were also disabled or suffering disease, were having fun. By fun I mean they were living lives that satisfied them. I wanted to be like them. How?

I didn't delude myself there were no problems. All life presents problems. I believe that life is about solving those problems. What are they? I mean, what are they with reference to aging, disability and sexuality?

The biggest problem I see is our culture. Our seemingly insatiable taste for youth and perfection is not real. Most of us are neither young nor perfect. Most of us, even the baby boomers, are coming of age. They, too, are coming to old age, if you will. Most of us live and love. We live together. We cohabit in different combinations: as husband and wife, man and man, or woman and woman. We all have sex. If others are uncomfortable with acknowledging sexuality in the aged and the disabled, young or old populations, that is their problem and not ours.

Ours is the right of every human being to be human. Ours, also, is the right to acknowledge, that as we age or become disabled, we are or are not interested in sex. This is a personal choice and not one the greater society can or should dictate.

The aging and disabled body must be taken into consideration. There may be pain or discomfort during sex. Thoughtfulness can produce the solution. Help in moving is available. Discussion with the partner is important. There are sexual aids readily available to help with dryness, penile dysfunction, and climax. Your doctor may be able to prescribe appropriate medication for your problem.

The aged and disabled are too often confined to institutions. Rest homes and hospitals do not provide the privacy we need for sex. Even in our own homes there may be limited privacy. Children and grandchildren, or caretakers, have to be considered. This is a problem we must face, and we have to fight for changes that will let us keep our human rights to the very end of life.

Finding a partner is not a problem peculiar to the disabled and aging. It is universal. But with us it may take more time and ingenuity. There is help: family, friends, community, and religious affiliations. I think that if we talk about it, the more we talk about it, the more open we become, the more the situation can be addressed and the problem solved. As they say: Seek and ye shall find.

Our children and some of our peers may be reluctant to understand. Now, in our seasoned years, we again face the embarrassment of talking to our children about sex. Not about how their sexual lives will be as they grow up, but about ours now that we are grown up. We did it then and we can do it now!

Sex and Privacy in the Hospital

Books, movies, and especially television have taught that there is indeed sex that goes on in hospitals. But the media shows only sex as practiced by doctors, nurses and other assorted personnel. It is never seen as a choice for patients. For this group, as far as public perception is concerned, sex is nonexistent.

From my own experience, both as a teacher in hospitals and rest homes and later as a patient, sex between patients, is considered an embarrassment, or a nuisance, or a problem.

But no matter how it is viewed, its practice exists. While I was recovering in a convalescent facility, my roommate was a man in his late thirties who was unable to walk, dress, or perform bodily functions without help. He was sharp of mind and wit, and had been hospitalized for many years following injuries received in accidents. His long-time residency had taught him how to get along and get what he wanted in the hospital. What he wanted was sex, and get it he did. His girlfriend was a woman who worked as an aide in another wing of the facility. She visited him on a regular basis, and I always left the room. The authorities winked and said nothing. But then again, this man knew the rules, and those included silence, not making waves, and arranging for his gratification on his own.

But what of those who needed assistance? Those who required at least privacy? While I was a teacher in a care facility, I knew of a couple whose respective spouses had "dumped" them to the care of others. They were confined to their chairs and could not get along without help. At first they managed to hold hands. And finally they found a way to engage in mutual masturbation. They told me how difficult it was to get any privacy, and certainly they could get no help from the staff.

I know of cases where staff has sedated the patient who showed signs of wanting to engage in sex. It occurs to me that no such restraints exist for the staff. They are allowed to have sex with whomever they wish, whenever they wish, and they have the ability to find the places in which to meet.

A solution is simple. Set aside rooms for conjugal visits. The prisons of this country recognize the value of such meetings and provide places. Why not our hospitals? The patient should be able to arrange for partners and for space, just as they are able to arrange for any other need, be it medical, as in getting treatment, or personal, as in getting a hairdresser.

Privacy has another face; it seems to be a given for everybody except the patient. Staff and visitors are always fully clothed. The patient is given a backless, shapeless garment that leaves private parts exposed. Attendants, nurses, or aides always see the patient nude, in showers, while changing clothes. The role is never reversed. Staff is given the right to pursue active sex lives. The patient is not. Even more damaging is when staff frown on any sexual activity, making fun of the patient and even telling others about the patient's experiences.

It is true that hospital residents require assistance in many bodily functions, and adaptations have to be made. It is not true that the patient must be put outside the pale of the world in which non-handicapped people function. It is a parallel universe, but it is not a separate one. Ramps and handgrips, wheelchairs and canes, and even eyeglasses and hearing aids are part of this other universe. Extending this way of thinking to bridging the gap, from disability to normal living, we need also to provide the ways and means to a healthy sex life. I have suggested only a few methods. The first steps must be changing attitudes towards the activity itself, looking on it as a way to healthy living, and arranging for accessibility to private places.

Section IV: Attitudes

*The greatest discovery of my generation is that
a human being can alter his life by altering his
attitude of mind.*

—WILLIAM JAMES

Taking Charge of My Life

What's the big deal? Doesn't everybody take charge of their own lives when they become adults? Didn't I? Well, to a point, I guess I did.

As a child and young man I had mother and father to help shape my life. Then my father was killed in an accident, and, at fifteen, I took charge of my life and that of my ailing mother.

I married and thought I was in charge of my life until the mother of our three children left us on our own. Then I was in sole charge of my life and that of my kids.

I thought I knew about being in charge. But nine years ago a CVA (commonly called a stroke) hit me unexpectedly. I was tied up to a million tubes in the intensive care unit at the hospital. I wasn't always aware of what was going on, but at one point I heard my doctor ask whether or not he should "pull the plug." He thought I would be a vegetable if I lived. I couldn't speak then, but I was determined to tell him NO. I do not know how I got that across but he did understand.

Then and there I took charge of my life, literally. I had decided I wanted to live and I was going to be in charge! What a challenge. If only I had known. Would I have done it differently? Absolutely not!

Ever since, I have lived fully. Although I had always been in charge of my life as an able-bodied person, I was now facing something new: How to do it as a disabled person.

I had to learn new ways to make my thoughts, needs and opinions understood. But since I couldn't speak, what to do? I tried many therapists. Some helped and some didn't. I eventually found one who set me straight, and I learned to talk again.

I also learned how important communication is, whether it is accomplished by speaking or writing. In all my past life and activities, I had never bothered to learn to type. But now, here I was unable to write in longhand. What to do? I went back to school, studied the computer, and learned to type (they call it keyboarding nowadays) with one hand.

This new skill enabled me to start writing about my experiences and to share with others what I had learned. I was lucky in finding publishers. My work has appeared in dozens of magazines and newsletters, and I have a chapter in two books. My partner and I are now putting together a book of our own.

I also looked for role models. Everybody thinks of Christopher Reeve, and he is wonderful. But I find him too far away. I like the people I meet daily who are living interesting lives. Being disabled is only one way to describe them. I know disabled people who are in school, studying to be lawyers, teachers, and counselors. I know others who work full-time at challenging jobs. I have one friend who teaches martial arts as self-defense even though a spinal cord injury left her with no movement in her legs. Another friend who was in her early thirties when a stroke cut short her doctoral program in bio-chemistry, can still do cartwheels on the beach. One man I know publishes a newsletter for stroke survivors.

These people confirmed what I learned about taking charge. I knew I needed physical therapy, and that meant exercise. I researched what was available, made an assessment of where I was weak, and began a rigorous program which I still follow. Maybe I was taking risks, but, after all, what is life if not an occasion to take a risk? I work out at a community college gym every day, lifting weights, riding the bicycle, and walking on a treadmill. I swim at a YMCA pool. For many years I was involved as a "lab rat" in the Veterans Administration's experimental programs.

Since my partner and I are both retired, we have the luxury of having time to enjoy that which we always liked. We go to the theatre, the opera, travel some, write, read a lot, and keep in touch with our friends and family.

I am convinced it pays to take charge and to take a few risks. There are a lot of us disabled people living independent and fulfilling life. It isn't only me. We don't have to do it alone. We can get help, but we are in charge of asking for it!

Don't Box Me In

Include me in! I want to work and play where everyone works and play. I believe that vitality lies in honoring differences, not simply in enjoying similarities.

I am a human being. I am a man. Over the years I have been a son, brother, husband, father, grandfather, friend, student, and teacher. I have been a psychologist, professor, writer, lecturer and cat lover.

I am also disabled. Does that make me different? I don't think so.

I do not want to be in a box labeled "disabled." I do want to be included in life. I want to be part of living in a community. I want to be included in work and play. I do not want separate but equal facilities. I want to be with any and all human beings, of whatever age, sex, race, creed, politics, and emotional disability. I want to be included in all community environments. I want to be included in recreational activities as well.

Our segregated society is ending. We have legal sanctions against discriminating or segregating according to race, gender, creed, and maybe even sexual orientation. The mainstream is still segregating recreational facilities for the disabled. But not all!

Across the country there is a movement called *Inclusion*. Models have been developed. There are a number of programs alive and well. An outstanding example of the inclusion program is found at the Saratoga, California YMCA. Under the direction of Dalia Nir, a program they call Physability is in place. The program is based on the philosophy that inclusion of disabled persons with the able-bodied population benefits all. By getting to know each other, we get to understand each other better. In a recent issue of the publication, *Institute for Community Inclusion*, Robin Foley had this to say about her disabled child:

"When I think of why my daughter should be included in education and recreation activities in our community, many things come to mind. I know that she will have fun and is motivated by learning from other children. I also feel it is important that she develop "broad shoulders" due to the initial reactions to her disability, which is a skill that will benefit her as an adult. Most importantly, through these experiences, my daughter will be making vital connections within the community by meeting the children who may someday be her neighbors, employers or fellow employees. Becoming linked as children will broaden future opportunities for both my daughter and children without disabilities by allowing their tolerance of differences to grow and fear to fade away."

As an adult, I have had my share of experiences in the larger community, when people stare at my wheelchair or talk to my companion instead of me, assuming I have no ability to communicate. It took a while for my friends, family, and me to learn what it means to be, and be with a disabled person. Including us in recreational activities broadens our chances.

I do not say that there should be no segregated areas for the disabled. In deep therapy, that may be important. I do say that we, the disabled, should have the choice of where we go to work out, to play, or attend community meetings.

I have found that, in working as an included person in the gym at the YMCA, I have grown in my understanding and so have the others. Being only with our own kind, in a segregated environment, leads to stagnation, not growth.

What to Do After the Doctor Leaves ... Or Caring for and by the Caregiver

By Roberta Johnson, J.D.

"I'm Gonna Live 'Til I Die." The old song filled my head. I could not remember any other words so I sang "I'm gonna live 'til I die!" Then, to my surprise, I sang: "And so is he."

"I" means me, Roberta "Bobby" Johnson, and "he" means my companion Dr. Thomas "Tom" Matola.

In September 1991, Tom suffered a severe stroke. The critical care unit was his home for weeks. For much of that time, survival was the only issue. Would he make it? Would he not? Hard times. He was a strong fighter, and he fought a good fight. I felt helpless. I did not know how to do anything but stand by. I did that. I felt I could do the ordinary things. I made the routine arrangements. I paid the bills. I kept in touch with the hospital, talking with the doctors, the nurses, the therapists. I kept in touch with our families and friends. I kept up with my job.

I filled out forms, applied for disability retirement and checked other possible insurance benefits. Anybody who has faced the task of taking care of a disabled person knows the work involved. This was difficult and time-consuming, but I had experience in dealing with such things.

What I didn't know how to do was what the professionals were doing. I didn't know how to dress him, take care of his personal hygiene, provide for exercise, give medicines, prepare his food, get him in and out of bed, and in and out of chairs. All of that I had yet to learn.

Six months after the stroke, when Rehab released him, I began my education. Tom had not only survived, he was very much alive. No more hospital, they told us. You can care for him, at home now. We were elated. But what was home? How could I care for him? He couldn't walk. His speech was indistinct. He could do very little for himself. Would I be able to take care of him?

At the time, I had a very demanding job for the state in Sacramento. I told myself I couldn't leave it. The truth was that I did not want to leave it.

What should we do? Fortunately, we could afford to hire people. That's a story in itself. How to survive some of the hired help is a tale worth telling—some other time. This article deals with the reality of taking care of a disabled person in his own home.

Just being available to do what needs doing isn't the whole story. Realistically, that must be the first consideration. What does he need? What does he want? They are not necessarily the same thing. For example, he may want all of my time, but I cannot give him that. He needs looking after, but I am not the only one who can do that.

What we did first was to start evaluating our needs and resources.

1. Did we need full-or part-time attendants? Did we need ramps, grab bars, telephone extensions? In other words: what physical arrangements would make life easier for both of us? In our case, we installed grab bars, moved the furniture around, and even put in hardwood floors when Tom could not maneuver the wheelchair on carpets.

2. How much money was available? This was difficult. Income from pensions would not be enough. We finally decided to sell some of Tom's property. This was unimproved land in Oregon where he had hoped to build a home someday. It had seemed a fair tradeoff. We had the funds for living life as we wanted to live it, and we did not want to move out of California.

3. I made conscious choices about how much of my time I could give. While working, I needed full-time help. After I retired, I used part-timers.

4. We investigated available therapies. We checked on community resources. We asked other disabled people about how they managed. We read the publications dealing with disabilities. We called and asked questions. We made choices based on what we needed and what we could afford.

5. We needed transportation, but what kind? We started with a car, and I learned how to transfer Tom to the front seat and put the folded wheelchair in the back. Later, we added a carrier for a motor scooter, and recently we bought a van with ramps and adaptive gear so Tom can learn to drive it. We had explored public transportation and decided on having a caregiver who could also drive.

6. I learned that all the things he and I had done without thinking now required a lot of thought. I talked with nutritionists about diet. Together, we learned how he could shave himself and take care of going to the toilet. I learned how to keep a calendar for his medical and dental appointments. We found a manicurist and a barber whose shops were easily accessible for the wheelchair. Tom and his dentist learned how to get him into the dental chair.

7. We found help from friends and family to sit with Tom when I was out for the day. We arranged for overnight care when I had to be away.

I learned the most important lesson of all. Even with help, it is I, as principal caregiver, who is totally responsible. If I cannot do it myself, I must arrange for someone else to do it. Remember that the outside helper can always call in sick or quit. So we have continued to prepare for things before they happen.

Importantly, Tom continues to learn to do things for himself. As he continues to improve, he takes over more responsibility for his care. He can now be alone during the day and can even arrange to get his own food. I have learned, and Tom keeps reminding me, that he needs the opportunity to have as much freedom and independence as possible.

My own sense of impatience gets in the way. It is easier for me to do the task than to watch him fumble. If I don't allow it, he cannot learn. He tells me I must not overdo for him, so he can regain as much control over his life as possible.

I have talked about the person receiving the care, but what about the caregiver? Yes, I mean, what about my needs? Do I subjugate my life to his? For a long time, I tried not to think about it. At first, there was no time. There was no question about priorities. First he had to live, and everything else, including my needs, took second place. When I realized he was going to live and we were both going to live until we died, I began to realize I would have to face the hard questions.

I really had to get to know myself. I made an inventory. It was a brutal evaluation. I tried to be rigorously honest. I looked for my strengths and my weaknesses.

Did I have enough love and passion to sublimate a large part of my life to his? I realized that my life would never be the same as it had been.

It was very hard. I wavered between feeling myself a martyr and then a traitor when I found resentment in my heart. It was also hard to be able to talk to Tom about these feelings. It is never easy to be open and honest about negative emotions. Fortunately, Tom is a psychologist and, for the most part, was able to deal with my frustrations. At times, he dealt with them better than I did. I would have tantrums! Mostly, he ignored me.

It was also hard to learn to talk about the limitations caused by finances. We learned to lower expectations. We bought a used van instead of a new one. We started to make choices and set priorities about how we did spend our money. We stopped eating out a lot. We chose to afford season tickets to the opera and the theater, because that is our passion.

The usually taboo subject of sex was easier for us. Tom earned his doctorate as a sexologist, and he and I could talk about what we could, and what we couldn't, do. I am grateful that we continue to enjoy our sex life together, as we do everything else.

The hardest thing for me was to talk to him about my wanting to get away. Although I am a retired administrative law judge, I still work on a pro-tem basis. Tom understood this, and it caused no problems.

Tom and I were avid hikers. He cannot do this anymore but I still can. At first I felt guilty because I wanted to continue hiking. We talked about it and he understood. I have regular days, each week, to get out on the trails. I participate in the Big Sur Walk and other organized events. When the walk is out of town, Tom comes with me and simply waits in the hotel. He is supportive of my sport.

I felt the need to get away for more than a day. We have talked this out and Tom understands. I now take an annual week's vacation on my own. I take a night away from home to visit with my daughter or friends.

None of this came easily, but we wanted to work things out and so we did. We still have problems; what couple doesn't? The truth is that when one has survived the sort of stroke Tom had, there is a sweetness to being alive, and the other things seem petty by comparison.

I have a friend who is paraplegic. He and his wife live in another state. She recently became ill and manifested signs of Alzheimer's. Her behavior was erratic and unpredictable. He was afraid to leave her alone. He developed an ulcer, like a bed sore, and did nothing about it because, as he told his sister, he had to look after his wife.

The ulcer became infected, and he is now in the hospital and will be there for about four months. The family has found a paid companion for his wife. The moral of the story: If we do not take care of ourselves first, we cannot take care of anybody else. More importantly, if we do not consciously take care of ourselves, our bodies may unconsciously find a way to force us to do so.

It is helpful, even necessary, to get emotional or psychological counseling. I have to deal with feelings of rage at times. I even get to feeling sorry for myself at times. I have had counseling, and I have friends I talk to. In my case, I am lucky. My best friend is Tom, and I can talk to him.

So, we keep singing and living. We really are living and will do so until we die.

Section V: Musings

My grandmother started
Walking five miles a day
When she was sixty.
She's ninety-five now
And we don't know where the hell she is.
                    —ELLEN DEGENERES

I Never Dream I Am in a Wheelchair

I never dream that I am in a wheelchair! Why? Because I have better places to be! I swim, I walk, and I dance. I even fly!

I know why I dream. There are no barriers in dreams. There are no limitations, physical, mental, emotional, or spiritual. I think that is what dreams are all about. They bring us back to better days. There is hope in their content.

Sometimes a dream is a great adventure into new realities where the environment is better, or nicer, than the undreaming state.

I think that for someone like me, limited in my movement, I get a shift in my reality. I make an "aha" discovery. I can get out of my bed, my chair, and my flights of fantasy are wonderful. I don't need a travel agent. I don't need a passport. I do not even need an itinerary. Everything that happens is lightened by spontaneity. I turn on my imagination, sprinkle it with fun, and away I go!

But there are the naysayers. There are those who say I must face the facts. I must accept who I am. True. I do that. But I also see nothing wrong in dreaming and projecting healthy positive pictures. I see nothing wrong in going for different scenery once in a while. I see nothing wrong in changing perspectives or mixing up time. It is great to visit friends and relatives who departed long ago, when they died or moved out of the neighborhood.

So my dreams are filled with me, a person who is whole. I do not have a weak arm or leg. I do the things I used to do and can do no more when I am awake. I also do the things I could not do very well then: I paint, play music, ski, run marathons, high dive, pilot a plane, or just fly.

I find I can control my dreams, somewhat. If I try too hard, though, they are gone. Years ago, before the stroke, I did some "out of body" work and was amazed at being able to look at myself from "out there." At those times I wanted to stay away. Now my dreams are like that, but they are different in that I wake up if the feelings become too vivid and intense.

Dreaming is healthier than taking drugs or alcohol. It is less expensive and the only possible side effect I can see is that I may never want to come back.

The dream state also reminds me of people who were diagnosed as catatonic when I worked in mental hospitals. I remember thinking they were in a world which they did not want to leave. But I felt they were in a prison, even if it was a benign one. No, I don't want that for myself. I like to dream because it gives me a vacation from the reality. But I find it also helps me deal with the reality upon my return.

The waking reality is my challenge. I accept that I must play the cards that were dealt me. Life goes on. How shall I use the time? I always visualized my future as one in which I contributed to humanity. I tried to live my life fulfilling that goal. That possibility still exists, I tell myself. I am no less a person now than I was before the stroke. I have limitations, but I also have possibilities. I suppose it is the "half empty/half full glass" syndrome.

As I study what has been written about dreams, I find a plethora of explanations. Some say they are wish fulfillments. Others find they are symbols and need interpretation for the reality they signify. Freud popularized the sexual aspects of dreams. I can live easily with all of the theories. I like to believe, and so I do believe, that the dream is an escape from an unpleasant reality, and I also believe that wish-fulfillment can be interpreted, symbolically, as a wish to regain the maximum recovery possible and so go on living fully. The sensual aspects of dreams are also instructive, since sexuality is a major part of my real life needs and desires. Dreams help lead the way to fulfillment.

As I dream, waking or sleeping, or even trying to meditate, I find I am the director, writer, and producer of the script. I review old scenes and change the endings I did not like. I make it better or I make it different. I play with it. It is my movie, and I am the hero who wins the pretty girl, fights the duels, staves off Armageddon, and does whatever will win the day and the applause.

I watch my cat sleeping, which he does most of the day. I watch him squiggle and hear him meow. Are they sounds and movements of joy? Of pain? Is he escaping? Is he sad, lonely, depressed? Or is he happy as he catches his moths on the fly? Who knows? I don't. It is enough to know he has his own dream life, as I have mine.

I do not mean to say that I have experienced only joy in my dreams. I have felt lots of pain and regret as well. Sometimes when I wake from an afternoon nap, I am astounded that I cannot get out of bed by myself. I have forgotten about the stroke. That is a painful moment. But like someone once said: we were never promised a rose garden. Even if we were, there are thorns that go with the flowers. I choose to concentrate on the red bud against the green leaf.

My world may be circumscribed by physical boundaries, but my dreams are not. I believe, with Shakespeare, that we are such stuff as dreams are made of. I say, with "Star Trek" Captain Jean Luc Picard: Make it so!

You Can't Get There from Here

If "here" is a given and "there" is an objective, the question is "how"?

Once, shortly after my stroke seven years ago, I was in Jacksonville, Oregon, a lovely and historic town I have enjoyed for many years. For the first time though, I was in a wheelchair. I tooled off the "cut" on one corner, intent on crossing the street. Not until I reached the other side did I notice there was no other cut. There was no way for me to access the sidewalk. I truly couldn't get there from where I was.

Paranoid thoughts overwhelmed me. Did they mean for me to be hit by a car? After all, then they wouldn't have to worry about accessibility for disabled persons. A shopkeeper, whose store was inaccessible, angrily defended her "rights" by telling my companion and me that they did not have to comply with the new ADA regulations because they were an "historical" town and had a "grandfather" exemption. So, if I got bumped off not being able to get there from here, I too, would be history.

The experience got me thinking about "accessibility" in general. In that Oregon town, somebody thought about making one corner cut. Was that just for minimal compliance with the law? If so, I think we are all in trouble. Because I know that ramps are not enough. Before we build those, we need to build understanding. We need to address what, for lack of a better word, we call "attitude."

Roget's New Thesaurus states that attitude is a frame of mind affecting one's thoughts or behavior. The Vietnamese Zen Master, Thich Nhat Hanh, reminds us of the "miracle of mindfulness." Thus, when we are mindful of our every moment our attitude will fashion rightful living.

When the human mind determined to place a cut on only one of four corners, had the attitude been correct, that human mind would have asked the purpose. The simple answer would have been evident. Being mindful of purpose, it would have known that another cut was needed to get from here to there.

We travel for business and pleasure. Most hotels have "accessible" rooms. Unmindful persons designed most bathrooms. These are the ones who thought of lowering the sink to wheelchair height. But they didn't think of the purpose, the full purpose, that is. They didn't think about use. Where do I put my shaver and toothbrush? No accommodation was made for a reachable shelf. They did not think clearly when they left no room to turn a wheelchair around.

They did not think clearly when they placed handicap rooms far from the elevator. One of the largest chain hotels did that, and a friend, who stayed there, could barely maneuver her walker a few feet at a time.

Movie houses, even the new ones, make us feel unwanted. Wheelchair seating is either in the last row or the first. To me, that is an unreasonable accommodation and an affront to my dignity.

Public agencies can be the worst. My friend, an articulate disability activist, attended a city council meeting. She is in a wheelchair. After a few hours of other speakers addressing the council, she was called. There was no way for her to access the podium. They placed a microphone near her seat. However, it was positioned so that she had her back turned to the decision-makers. They did not have to look into her eyes as she pleaded the cause of the disabled community. This insult was preceded by her having to park her van in the furthest spot from the city hall, as there was no closer disabled parking space.

People who install public toilets do put grab bars in their commodes. Why, then, oh why, don't they put enough bars up? Frequently I find the bars placed for use by a right-handed person. My right side was affected by my stroke. I need the bar on the left side! Why put the toilet upstairs and provide no elevator. No way can I reach that necessary accommodation. I found this in restaurants in San Francisco and San Jose. Both managers were surly when asked about it. In fact, one became angry. I think that response was to somehow justify his position to me.

The Bible tells us to do unto others as they would do unto us. My parents reminded me often, when I was a child, that others will treat me as I treat them. Because only one out of six people today has a disability, there may not yet be cause for reciprocal dealings. But since we are all subject to sudden temporary or permanent disability, it is in our self-interest to develop attitudes of understanding. We must learn to be mindful of our thoughts and actions. We must address the questions of getting there from here and doing it safely.

Spend a day in a wheelchair. See how simple things like getting into a bathroom become complex. Notice how the doors are not wide enough to accommodate a chair. See how doors open in or out. Check the door weight. Can a person with disabilities use that door?

As we sow, so shall we reap. Now, while one is able-bodied, is the time to prepare. It costs money, they say. Of course it costs money. Everything costs money. And it costs much more money to make adjustments after disability happens. Now is the time to think about universal accessibility in housing, in shopping centers. As new building continues, we could see to it that the facilities are disabled-friendly. As the general population ages, the disabled population increases. After all, the alternative is to die young.

Yet our life span does go from here to there and we need each other to reach there. I see it as a bridge of understanding. The temporarily able-bodied persons can start now to prepare. It's like investing in the stock market or opening a retirement account. We have hopes for the future, and we do something concrete about assuring the goal. We all, disabled and temporarily able-bodied persons, are in this together. I urge us to play the game fairly, and mindful of all consequences.

Color Me ... Please

Color me purple! Color me blue! Color me green or yellow! But please, add color to the white!

I didn't always hate the white. As a matter of fact, I usually didn't think much about it. So how did I come to the sheer horror, and sometimes terror, I feel when I see white, especially white walls?

It all started in a hospital room. The stroke was sudden, grabbing my life in a moment. Taking me from my home, which was colorful, to the white-walled, white-ceilinged, white-robed environment of an alien place. It didn't matter too much at first, when I had only to survive, moment by moment. I had no time to think or dream about quality of life. At that moment, only the quantity that remained concerned me.

And I am grateful. I thank those who inhabited that white world for their help in bringing me back. I almost feel guilty faulting any of them. But I must speak of the six months after the first six weeks that I spent "in hospital." Although I have some good memories, I also remember feeling abused, neglected, and degraded. It wasn't a comedian's line when I said, "I get no respect." Aside from a few exceptional people, I remember those to whom I was a number, a room number, a medical record number, or the guy who can't talk or move.

As I look back, now that I am a stroke survivor who tries to live every moment as a life in progress, I am impelled to speak out. I am angry. I want to join in some kind of "power" movement. Like "black power," "power to the people," and women's rights. I join with others abjuring the niceties of language. I call myself a "crip." I say that with dignity, because there is nothing wrong in being a cripple. I have my rights, same as anybody else. We are a fast-growing population. We must not let anyone put us out of sight, out of sound. We must be seen, heard, and counted. We must make sure nothing is done about me, without me!

So I tell my story of how the system treated me. The intensive care unit was sterile and white, but I was too sick to notice. Out of intensive care and onto the "floor" was my next step. Again white walls and uniforms. The only greenery was from the flowers brought by friends and relatives. I began to yearn for my gardens at home. I could barely move and could not talk at all, but I wanted out. I prevailed upon them to send me to a rehabilitation facility, located out of my area. In the five weeks I was there, I had to be strapped in my chair, and fed my food, and I could only communicate using an alphabet card. The attendants were busy and couldn't see to my individual needs.

Accordingly, when I made too much noise trying to breathe at night, they put me in a storage room, where I was by myself, so the others in my ward would not be disturbed. They never asked how I felt about that. The truth is that I was very frightened to be alone. I couldn't talk, and I felt nobody would take the time to read what I spelled out on an alphabet card.

One day a nursing aide took my temperature. As she placed a glass thermometer in my mouth, I tried to communicate that it would break since I couldn't control spasms. Even if I could have spoken, she would not have understood English. The thermometer did break. A bloody mouth and a rush to x-rays followed. Fortunately the injuries were minor, as far as the physical body was concerned. Not so fortunately, my psyche was damaged. The incident underscored my fear of being totally dependent on strangers, who seemed incompetent and uncaring.

The rehabilitation facility had strict standards, and I failed their tests. I showed little or no improvement. I was asked to leave and enter a skilled nursing center.

The first day there was a mixed blessing. The physical therapy staff greeted me with warmth, affection, and hope. The lead physical therapist had me on my feet, supported by an aide, and walking a few steps. They used a string tied to my leg. It was like a lead rope. It worked. They fed me my favorite food, a lox spread, as a reward for my slightest improvement. I stayed six months and came to love the physical therapy people. They knew my name, they knew who I was, and they showed they cared.

Holidays were bad. I was more than a hundred miles from my home, and no family or friends made the trip. I couldn't swallow at that time so all food was "pap." Pretty tasteless. White bread, indeed!

At Christmas, one of my therapists brought her husband, mother and children to see me. I was very touched by their kindness.

The incident reminded me that the longer one was away from home the longer were the absences of family and friends. It seems people forget. They have busy and full lives. The hospital patient has a busy and full schedule, if he is lucky. But he has no life outside the hospital.

The life inside the hospital was made up of small and large struggles. At that time, smoking was allowed and the recreation room was a smoke-filled, noisy, almost raucous place. I couldn't stand it. I had to struggle with myself to shut out the yells and cries of other patients, especially those who could utter only obscenities.

My therapy sessions were my salvation, but I had to be up and dressed. The staff didn't seem to care. I was late many times, and sometimes I had to miss the session entirely. I groused continually, and I am not a particularly complaining person. One thing on my side was having my partner, who is an attorney, as my advocate. I strongly urge all patients and their families to make sure there is an advocate on hand.

My partner reminded the administration that neglecting to dress the patient in time for a therapy session was not merely rude or unthinking, but was a callous disregard of professional responsibility and could amount to a charge of patient neglect. They listened when she talked.

I began to notice a hierarchy in the staff. At the top was the administrator. The physicians were not resident, but were on-call only. Registered nurses were few, and they had little contact with the patients. They seemed to have become the bookkeepers, recording doctor orders, drugs given, and God knows what all else. They seemed to be always writing something down. The registered nurses talked to the doctors and sometimes the licensed vocational nurses. These LVNs had some patient contact, but very little. It was left to the nursing assistants to give the day-to-day, moment-to-moment, one-on-one care to the patient. While I recognize that there is a shortage of help for these low-paying jobs, I also recognize the huge problem caused by language gaps. Many of the aides spoke English poorly, if at all. Communication is all-important to the disabled person who must depend on getting his needs met by telling someone about them. The frustrations were endless.

I also noticed, during my hospital stays, that the doctors and nurses were the pessimists. Or at the very least, they, in the interest of "not raising hopes" would not, or could not, say anything about the possibility that the future might be bright. I found this hard to take, as I feel it is important to put a positive spin on situations and look for the good side of things. Hope, I believe, must be kept alive. I found the physical therapists different. They were encouraging. They celebrated minor victories as I learned to use a new muscle or take a new step. They helped me keep my faith that hard work and application to my therapy would yield results. And it did.

I am living a full life. I go to movies, the opera, and the theatre. I visit friends. I travel. I move in a wheelchair, but I do move about. I exercise every day. I swim and ride a horse. I am able to read, study, lecture, and write. I feel

I am productive. I have a name that people know, and they call me by that name.

The hospital experience is now behind me and yet I still gripe. Why? Because I can now fully appreciate how important it is to be cared for in the home. After all, if the nursing homes are so good, why do most people who are asked say they would rather die than go into a home? But the system doesn't understand that yet. Instead of putting money into the sterile, "white" world of the convalescent hospital, put that money into home care. At home, the individual can be looked after in a place of color. After all, color is the essence of life. It is communication. It is caring. It is also probably cost-efficient. Now, at home and in my seventh year of recovery, I appreciate being alive. A brief one-day stay in the hospital last year brought back the old memories, and I was thankful I could get out so soon. At home, I have a loving companion and a loving cat. We three live together in harmony and in color. Only the ceilings in my house are white. Every other room now boasts a vibrant color: yellow for the kitchen, dark green for my study, blue for the bedroom, and purple for the connecting hall. My gardens are filled with blossoming bushes and resplendent annuals and perennials. Most of my tulips are purple. The banner for "disabled rights" that I carry is painted in psychedelic colors. It is a flag to carry proudly!

My Spiritual Journey

My quest for truth, belief, religion, has been a tor-turous one. It has taken many turns, some of them quite strange. I still seek answers, but now I know and believe many things that keep me at peace with my soul.

I began my religious life in conflict. Not mine, but that of my parents. My father was of the Ukrainian Orthodox faith. My mother subscribed wholeheartedly to the teachings of the Roman Catholic Church. Each parent labeled the other "heretic." To keep the peace, my father allowed my mother to prevail in my early religious education.

Even so, there were conflicts. I celebrated two Christ-mases and two Easters. I think this made me emulate my patron saint. I became a doubting Thomas. I had problems with equating the Christian teachings of both religions with the common practices of shopping for presents in the malls. There seemed to be no real connection with the teachings of Jesus and the gaudy decorations and hectic festivities of the season. I could not see or understand the connection between Easter bunnies, really a fertility rite, and the death and resurrection of the Savior. What, I wondered, did the meaning of those two holidays have to do with buying new clothes or coloring eggs.

When I married a woman who was religious enough to have once wanted to be a nun, I kept the faith for the sake of our marriage and our three children. But I continued to have my doubts reinforced. Once, when I had been given a beautiful family bible, I took it to a priest for blessing. He told me in all righteousness that only the priests of the Church could interpret the Bible and that I was not fit to do it. I felt rebuffed and rejected. Why did he think I could not think for myself? Why was he trying to discourage me from thinking for myself? Earlier, I remember my anger and anxiety as a priest told me my mother would go to hell because she did not attend church regularly. She was, a that time, bedridden and unable to do so. Nevertheless, the priest could find no forgiveness for her. I, too, was damned. I did not go to Sunday services because I was then a weekend warrior with the Air National Guard, and my duties kept me busy on Sunday.

The Roman Catholic Church continued to confound my belief. My wife left the children and me for someone else. Although I had kept my marriage vows, religiously, and she had not, I was the one who was refused communion and the community of the church activities. It was then I started my search for my soul and my spirituality in earnest.

Many of my friends then were Jewish. They were much more accepting of me, as I was, than the Catholic community of my former church. So I studied Judaism and I also studied other Christian practices. I liked the ecumenical movement. I liked the idea of joining existing religious practices, because I always did believe in a God power. I was learning not tolerance of others' beliefs, but a deeper understanding and appreciation of them. I married again, this time to a woman who had not been a practicing Jew, but through my urging became one. We were married in a reform ceremony, but used the Jewish wedding customs. I liked being married under the canopy. I liked wearing the yarmulke. I liked teaching classes and working with Rabbi Levy. I did not convert. I was not asked to. I was simply accepted for who I was and that was good enough for me.

That marriage was a brief one. Its ending sent me on a further search. This time I became involved in the activities of a Unitarian church. I found I could keep my connection to Judaism there, and that was important for me. I also expanded my religious studies. I looked into spiritual healing. I joined a church of religious science and almost became a practitioner. But I could not pass one of the tests. I could not pass their test of naming the symbols. That was all right with me since I was interested, not in the symbols, but in the practice itself. I studied about reincarnation. I do believe there is much evidence to support such a belief. I participated in Buddhist retreats. I studied Hinduism. I traveled with psychics, went into past lives, traversed the universe to the planet of Venus, where two of my friends said they came from and who told me I had been their pilot to get to Earth. I met persons who are from Atlantis and others who live on air only, not on food. I met with witches, and even dated one for a while.

I took a psychedelic trip without taking drugs. It happened on a clothing optional beach on the San Francisco peninsula. My friends and I sat in a circle as we meditated together. I shot out to outer space, where I and the flashing colors and stars became one.

I experienced another unity in space. While meditating at a Buddhist retreat center, I envisioned a spider and clearly saw his hanging line. I became that spider. I saw the world through his eyes. In that way, I could separate myself from the discomfort I was feeling sitting in the lotus position for many hours. I have learned this value in meditating: Today I can be free of my stroke-induced crippled body by leaving it for a trip into beautiful space. Was it all real? Were they only illusions?

Was it my delusion? It really does not matter to me. I know there is something more than me in the universe. I like the idea of reincarnation. It makes sense to me. I have experienced past lives. I believe I have lived as a Chinese woman during the Boxer rebellion. I believe I was buried alive during the plague, that a tiger in India ate my sister, and later I was a tiger hunter making love on a tiger skin.

I still do not really know. Not for sure, that is. But I do not deny any of it. I know what is very real to me is my belief in the balance of nature and of natural forces. I feel physical pain when I see the rape of the earth. Man is murdering the planet with overpopulation. Burning forests are now downing airplanes when pilots cannot see to land. The ozone layer is destroyed. I believe a master builder made this beautiful planet. I believe we are meant to be its caretakers. Why are we failing? What must we do?

This now becomes part of my quest for religion. I believe there is a God, a great teacher we can call Christ, or any other name, and that we need to heed the injunction to be Christ-like. We need to find love and the solution to living together in peace and in serenity and with a plan for all people to survive together here on Earth. We need, I believe, this sort of faith, and we need, I also believe, to start using the 99% percent of the brain scientists tell us we do not use.

Feeling anger at man's intrusion, I feel close to the Druids and to the pantheism of the Indians. They were ones who respected nature, protected it, and lived within its laws. And so do I.

My Life-giving Garden

My garden is pretty. It is lovely to look at. It is a joy! I love its smells. I love its touch. I love when it speaks to me.

Most of all, I know it lives, breathes, comforts, and instructs. It fills the senses and it fills the soul; it awakens the mind and mirrors the universe.

My plants are my friends, the companions of my wheelchair-bound days. They offer no combat, no back talk, just appreciation for my attention and my love.

I begin each day with my back yard, outside my bedroom window. I have limited mobility, so I need help in actually digging and planting. But I alone visualize the plan. I tend the ferns, the climbing fuchsias, the birds of paradise, the hardy geraniums, the tomatoes, oleanders, coleus, impatiens, and more too numerous to name.

Whatever the season, the colors are glorious. My right side was affected by my stroke, and I can no longer put a brush to canvas. But I can utilize nature's palette to paint. The earth nurtures the forms and brings forth the colors I have visualized. The fence is not only the frame, but a backdrop for the hanging geraniums, passion vines, and sculptures.

Since they are all alive, it seems only right that I give them names. Say "hello" to Red Hot Rosie, Felicity Fuchsia and, Geraldine Geranium.

Later in the day, I tend to my side and front gardens. All the spaces are small, surrounding my house on three sides. I have only one neighbor. We share the park across the street, which is a lovely open space. The original Japanese settler conceived it as a holy place. A giant oak dominates, surrounded by pines. It is inhabited by squirrels; more about that furry creature later.

At the side, where I get the most sun, I have my rose bushes. I have red, yellow, pink, white, and silver roses in abundance all summer and on into the fall. Here also are the gallant gardenia and azalea bushes, planted in a center spot across from the espaliered prune and fig trees. In moveable tubs, I have an orange and lemon tree. The fence supports a Japanese box hedge, which I have carved into the shape of a heart.

I find it hard to cut the flowers because they are so perfect where they bloom. But I know they will wither, and so I like to think they will enjoy giving me joy when I arrange them in vases and bring them into the house. One day, when the cat kicked over an inside arrangement, I left them on the patio table. Like Lamb's discovery of roast pig, it was a fortuitous accident. The cut flowers still seemed to be where they belonged, outside, in the sun and in the breeze. I now regularly arrange them in that fashion.

My garden is a place of quiet and solitude. It is here that I meditate and muse. I find the business of the outside world intrudes on the core of my being. In my garden I find peace and quiet. Here it is that I can hear the sound of my own voice, and even the sound of one hand clapping.

In moments of depression, which come more often than I like since the stroke, I find the strength to go on. In moments of stress, also harder to handle since the stroke, I find the surrender to the beauty around me gives me the ability to release and to go on.

Seeing the design of the creator in the garden, I recognize that we live on this planet, not as masters, but in harmony with everything around us. To destroy nature is to destroy the universe, and we cannot win that game. We can only fathom that unfathomable by surrendering and caring about what happens.

I watch the plants grow, bloom, and die. I talk to them. I listen to them. Bound by my wheelchair I can understand what it feels like to be in a place I do not want to be. How can I be moved? Do they want to be moved? It is then I hear, and maybe it is fanciful, the plant asking to be moved. I comply, dig up, and replant. I administer vitamins, watch the water flow, and I especially look to see if it likes its new home. I can always tell. Many times I am rewarded by seeing larger, brighter blooms, greener leaves, and taller stems.

I also grow vegetables, herbs, and grapes. In my front space, I have wine grape vines on the fence. My Thompson seedless grapes share space on the overhead trellis with my bougainvillea, hibiscus, and wisteria. They look good and taste good. The hummingbirds and I are ecstatic, both of us a little bit drunk on the thought of consuming the nectar.

The tomatoes add a sweet smell to the salads, as well as making a delicious dish. Italian sauces go on my pasta, full of fresh basil, rosemary, chives, cilantro, thyme, all from my herb garden.

I am so full of my garden and its sensual pleasures that I sometimes surprise myself with musings of a more philosophical nature. Not too many years ago, I witnessed a developer in the southern California desert directing his mammoth machines to dig deep into the beautiful brown hills. Each thrust hurt so badly I cried. In the name of progress and "bottom line" accounting, we rape the earth and what it gives us. In that climate vintners were growing their grapes. They told me how worried they were by the encroaching building, bringing not only noise but pollution of the air and the precious, scarce water. I cried again.

Now as I sit in my gardens, I muse on the destruction "out there" where I feel helpless to help. So in my gardens, I am "in here" and I can do something to nurture myself and my neighborhood. I recently planted a color "garden" along a fence seen by my neighbors. The vibrant hues of roses, margaritas, and zinnias bring smiles to all who look. A friend asked where the fairies and elves were. I know they live in that particular spot.

Also living in my gardens are frogs, toads, and, woe unto me, squirrels. The frogs are actually in my neighbor's pond, and they serenade me at night. They chirp, in unison, and stop for a breath, in unison. The sound and the silence occur in even spurts. They lull me to sleep, and when I am out of town I miss them. My toad, Freddie, moves from garden to garden, depending on the weather. I saw him once. Very big, very ugly, very toad-like indeed. I have seen him only that once, but I hear him and welcome him.

The squirrels are another story. They and I are at war. They have managed to get into every bird feeder I have put up. They drink the water in the fountain. Once, last winter, the water froze, and it was fun to see them attempt to skate on the surface. Mostly I yell at them to go away. They pay me no mind at all. I have watched them bury walnuts they get from a neighborhood tree in my potted plants, and then the next winter forget where they did that. My cat, T.K., likes to watch them. And truth to tell, I don't know what I'd do if they left.

All in all, my gardens are my windows into the universe, engaging all my senses. The back garden is a symphony of silence serving as background for the sounds of the birds, bees, and animals who live or visit me. My front garden is a brass band, its crescendo of screaming color, loud and boisterous. The feast for the eyes is bright. The nose picks up the scent of rose, jasmine, gardenia, and heliotrope. The palate is tickled by the tomatoes and pungent herbs. The tactile senses glory in the feel of the dirt and the leaves. And like the universe, my garden is born, dies, and is reborn, with each season. And each rebirth is, to me, beautiful and a testament to that power I can only call my higher power.

Tom's gardens

What's Wrong with Vanilla Sex?

The "sexual revolution" brought with it many changes in our culture. I feel most have been healthy. More openness about sexual behavior, for example, is an advantage. The disadvantage is that it has also brought with it more expectations and consequently more complications.

Every issue of the popular magazines of the day has at least one article giving twenty-one ways to make your relationship more fun or more challenging or more daring. They challenge readers to try new positions, new partners of either sex, or new combinations of participants. Sexual play now must have toys: visual, olfactory, or auditory stimulation; rings in various body orifices; sado-masochistic techniques; the use of fabrics and feathers; and much more.

However, I am here to argue for good old-time sex: Sex between consenting, loving adults. Sex I have come to call "vanilla sex."

As a graduate student at San Francisco's Institute for the Advanced Study of Human Sexuality, I found myself the oddball. On the Kinsey scale, I measured on the totally heterosexual side. I had and have no trouble accepting others who are homosexual or bisexual. For the most part, my tolerance was not reciprocated. What were they advocating? Here's a partial list:
1. Mutilation
2. Tattoos

3. Rings on fingers, toes, nipples, belly buttons, penis, labia, and other places I never imagined.
4. Imitating postures from the Kama Sutra
5. Costumes, make-up and make-believe
6. Fantasies, shared or singular
7. Porno films
8. Multiples orgasms
9. The one-hour-or-longer-orgasm
10. Bondage
11. Toys
12. Whipped cream
13. Multiple partners
14. Serial monogamy
15 Polygamy
16. Incense
17. Assorted paraphernalia
18. Other "kinky" stuff I won't mention

Now, I am not denying their tastes. They like tutti-frutti. And I like vanilla. I like vanilla and I am glad!

For me, sex is joyful. It is a relaxing time. There are no power games, and it is not a war zone.

I don't have to strain for a fantasy. It is great if I have one, but what is wrong with being in the moment with my love? What is wrong with being only with her, and not with the toys?

I do not spend money or time in getting and arranging the toys, videos or books. I do not prepare food or buy leather or perfume.

Love is any time. I do not need to schedule the time and place.

I do not have to remember the lessons of Psych 101.

I think it is okay to laugh and be happy, not serious. It feels good to be spontaneous, acting as an artist and not a technician.

So, what is the big deal?

For me, my sexual turn on is being with my lover, in

her woman's presence, her touch, her smell, her taste. I am aroused. We laugh and we play. We are together in the moment. We do not need toys. We do not need other stimulation. In our love, we know what pleases the other. We explore and experiment together.

I talked of this to my fellow students. They dubbed me a "square." I was not exciting. I disagree. I find my sex life exciting enough. As Dr. Ruth says. "Sex is not just for procreation, but for recreation." So. Have a quickie sometime. Do not take it out of proportion. Enjoy, as we enjoy a fine wine with a fine dinner: Some of the time. And some of the time we like pizza and beer.

I have only two rules about sex. First it must be consensual and second it must be enjoyable. As a sexologist, I know about all sorts of sexual behaviors. I acknowledge them and salute those who, without harming others, indulge in the practices. But give me a break. I salute, with a 21-gun salvo, those who practice vanilla sex!!

Beam Me Up, Scotty. Please!

Each day's news brings added evidence there is no intelligent life here on earth. I want out. I want up and away, Scotty.

I don't belong here. Years ago, that proof came to me in the form of two aliens. I'll call them Robert and Claire. I met them at a conference of some sort. I don't remember the topic, but it is not important. I was destined to meet them. Claire, a wraith-like figure dressed in gauzy airiness, approached in a warm rush. She was so glad to see me again. I was her husband, she said. Since I was not then married, I raised an eyebrow. Oh, she said, we were not wed in this space. We had been married on Venus. I was the pilot of the space ship that brought us all, me, her, and her present husband to earth. We came from Venus, she told me. Didn't I remember?

Well, no, I didn't remember, but why not? I liked them both. At that time I worked as a psychologist at a mental hospital and I was used to space travelers of all sorts. So I went along for the ride. We became friends. They were both teachers, but they soon quit their jobs because they had received word that a space ship was coming to take them home to Venus. They were to be picked up in New Mexico. I visited them there. They had bought a beautiful home. It was a restored adobe building with thick walls; skylights open to the starry New Mexico heavens, fireplaces in every room, and fragrant gardens. Robert was working as a clothing salesman to while away the days. Claire was looking after him and seemed a bit worried about him. He talked of going home to Venus and of hearing voices telling him where the ship would be landing.

They later moved to Colorado because those voices told him that was where the ship would land. I lost track of them; my letters returned marked "unknown." I think they probably finally did make contact and are safely and happily home away from this planet.

Oh, how I envy them. I hear of construction in the desert and mountains, the land being raped. I listen to people on Earth prate about justice, honor, freedom, value; but they don't talk about the greed, about having a record number of billionaires side-by-side with a record number of homeless. I read of the growing violence in the world, of the holy wars.

How can God want death and destruction? I believe God wants love. I can handle the effects of the El Niño, because that may well be God's will, a force of nature beyond our control. But we can, if we only would, control the wanton destruction of nature's beauty and of human lives.

I miss Robert and Claire. I want to go home, too. Oh, beam me up, Scotty, please.

Tom, the Teddy Bear Therapist

I like my cluttered desk. It is a memory trigger. It is there, in the open, where I put the bits and pieces of the important events in my life. And so, when I see the gold badge that says I am "TOM M. THERAPIST," I remember the wonderful ten years I spent working in a mental hospital.

And I remember also the ending, when I suffered a stroke and was hospitalized for six months. My friends from the hospital, staff and patients, sent me cards and gifts, and some even visited. They brought signs for the glaring and boring white walls. My room was x-rated. They brought off-color jokes and sexy pictures to pin up. The nurses couldn't decide if they should laugh or expel me. The greatest gift was a book they wrote. Although many of the patients wrote things only found in the dreams and fantasies of mentally ill persons, I could clearly read their message. It was love they talked about. And that love helped me maintain my sanity in the nightmare that was my recovery.

And I loved them. Oh, how I loved them. I started out as a teacher assigned by the local school district. But the role of teacher turned into therapist very quickly. At that time, I had my master's degree in psychology and had experience as a psychologist in mental facilities. My class became a group-therapy session.

I have always liked to play, and I like stuffed animals. Soon, I started bringing teddy bears with me to the group session. My favorite was Theodora, whose creator had picked her especially for me. She was the leader. Anybody could tell her anything. I perceived that she was less threatening than puppets, a tool long used in treatment. My group knew, deeply, that Theodora would never, never tell what they told her. And as I listened, I learned what was happening in the life of that group member.

Other bears I brought with me joined Theodora. The patients and the bears talked and talked and told each other things they never would have told me. As Theodora talked through me, I could tell them things they would not have accepted from another patient, parent, or therapist.

They called me the "teddy bear therapist," and the other staff were skeptical. But nothing succeeds like success and my group kept improving.

I added another dimension, which was considered a "no-no." I started to hug my patients. I had met Leo Buscaglia once and he convinced me that touching each other was important and was especially important in healing emotional problems. I was careful. Many of my patients had exhibited violent behavior at times. They had been diagnosed as schizoid paranoid. Although I trusted them, I always had an orderly in the room with me. The bigger the orderly, the safer I felt. He or she was there to assist in case the patient acted out or became ill. Fortunately, in all my ten years there, such a problem never occurred.

Although I knew these people were mentally ill and had been confined for that reason, I never knew, nor did I want to know, their specific histories. Like teachers looking at the IQs of their students, I didn't want expectations that could be self-fulfilling. I did not need to know. It was enough to know them as they were at that moment. They were persons, individuals, with names, and we loved each other.

I believe that love and trust and truth are healing agents. I believe these perspectives can work the same miracles in our everyday relationships.

When we feel we cannot trust the press, the television cynics, the government, the Internet, or whatever else is today's bogeyman, then we can trust the teddy bear. My bears now live with me, in my study in my home. They grace my bookshelves, about 50 or 60 of them. Theodora is the central figure. My cat, loving by nature, sometimes attacks my bears. I know he doesn't hate the bears, but is just trying to attract my attention. So I give a bear to him and peace reigns once more in my study.

About seven months after my stroke, my former colleagues at the hospital where I had taught, invited me to a party. It was my first outing since my release from the rehabilitation center. I could barely keep my head up, but I managed to stand up when they announced my presence and awarded me the gold badge.

I am as proud of that as I am of the doctorate degree I earned after my stroke. In many ways, I learned more from my patients than I did from my professors.

I learned about love and acceptance and endurance. These important lessons, which I could never have learned in the halls of academe, sustained me in my recovery. The teddy bears, the patients, and "Tom M., Therapist" still prevail!

Tom in his study with part of his hat and teddy bear collection.

Tom, the Teacher

The carved wooden placard, hand made by teen-aged mentally-challenged boys, announces that I am "Tom the Teacher."

My academic degrees are in psychology and sexology, and yet I am most proud of being a teacher. I didn't pursue teaching as my first career, but it was what I did anyway and what I find, now that I look back on the decades behind me, to be the work I most enjoyed.

It started by accident. My father had died in an accident. My two older brothers were in the Army. I was left to look after my mother. Wanting to be like my brothers, but too young to enlist, I did the next best thing. I joined the Reserves. They put me in the Signal Corps. My job was to climb poles. At first it was fun. It was adventurous and daring being high in the sky. Then one day, I fell. It was not fun any more.

What to do? I learned I could teach pole-climbing at low heights. Somehow I impressed the army brass, because they put me in charge of training in an air corps command teaching air police medics.

I was good at mathematics and learned navigation and became a navigator.

The teaching got me new jobs in the Air Corps and a nomination to officer's candidate school. I found the work easy and graduated at the top of my class. The high command ordered me to teach why we were in the Korean conflict. I could not do it. I did not believe in the war and I did not believe we could rationalize our being there. Therefore, I could not teach it. They said I had the wrong attitude. I agreed. I could not follow blindly. I gave up my commission. I quit!

It seemed whatever I did I could transfer to teaching. While in the Reserves, I decided I needed help in meeting women. I went to dance schools and got good enough to win a tango competition. I found that my ability to keep time in dancing helped me when I became a drill instructor for the troops. As such, I won a coveted spot on the Freedom Train and got to wear an elegant uniform and travel around the country.

While still serving in the Reserves, I became a police officer. I enjoyed this for a while. Then they asked me to train in arrest methods. I found these methods were brutal. I certainly did not believe in them and I refused to teach them. I quit!

About this time a new field was opening: Semiconductors! Not many people knew about them and fewer knew how to train personnel in their applications. For me it was a daring challenge. A chip-making company, A.M.I., gave me a job to administer its training program. What did I know about chips? Nothing. I read books, magazine articles, and toured the factory. I learned enough to be able to teach about it and in a few weeks I started training new employees.

I have been using the words "training" and "teaching" interchangeably. I need to define these words. However used, I mean that what I do and what I want to do is to facilitate learning. My Air Force and A.M.I. experience taught me that the key to teaching is not to "teach" but to get the process of learning started. I do not transfer the learning to you but instead I help you get from me what you need to learn for yourself.

This principle worked well with Vietnam War veterans. My assignment was to get them ready to live civilian lives after leaving the hospital. All men, they had serious emotional, mental, and physical problems.

Many were alcoholic or drug-addicted. After therapy, they wanted to go out into the world and live on their own. They did not know how to do that. We called my program Purple Heart. I believed deeply in what I was doing, so the fact that my only training for this job was that I knew how to live independently myself, was enough.

We built a model home inside an old warehouse. It had the usual rooms, including a kitchen and bathroom. We did the basics: laundry, ironing, cleaning the house and our own bodies, brushing teeth, and shaving. We read the newspapers and checked grocery ads. We made up menus for dinner and shopped together for the best prices. We cooked what we bought, served it with the proper plates and silverware, and ate it, as a celebration. What an accomplishment!

We wrote resumes and held mock interviews for jobs. Not all, not even most, but at least some, learned and did go out into that world they wanted to join. A political move canceled the program. I felt the loss deeply, but I was able to go on to other things. Those men, who needed to learn basic living skills, could not. It hurt then, and it hurts now, to think about it.

Recently the woman who had been my assistant in that program called. After many years she still credits our work together as a great learning time. She told me she had stayed in the field of helping people and continues to serve the community.

I went on to teach at Agnew State Hospital. My students were young boys who had been rejected by their families and were wards of the state. They, too, wanted to go out into the bigger world. We did that by teaching them a trade. They were adept at woodworking, and my reward was the sign "Tom the Teacher." I am as proud of that as I am of the dozen or so teacher certificates that also hang on my walls.

I worked at Lockheed for eleven years. I was in the Apollo Manned Orbital Laboratory, and it was exciting. It was still the early stages of the space program. I met the first astronauts. My job was as a human factors engineer, and my area of concern was safety for the astronauts.

Again it was a teaching-learning experience. I had to find out from them what was needed for safety purposes, and they had to learn from me how to adapt. I believed in the space program, then and now, and had a wonderful time.

It came to an end when Lockheed wanted me to work on submarines. They particularly wanted me to design a system making it impossible to fire an atomic rocket, or missile, by accident. This was on the Poseidon project. An accidental launch, aimed at our enemy of the time, Russia, would start World War III. We called this sort of design an attempt to "idiot-proof" the system. I conceived the idea of having two keys under a cover over the launch button. One key was with the ship or submarine commander, and the other with the launch, or firing, officer. Both keys would be needed, and both would react only to the command of the President of the United States. I was unhappy with the solution.

Indeed, I felt there was no foolproof or "idiot-proof" solution. Even with all possible safeguards in place I felt it would still be possible for some drunken, mad, or fanatic human being to start global devastation. I did not want to be part of the game. That fear contributed to the claustrophobia I was already feeling in the cramped quarters of the sub. I had no choice, in my mind, but to quit and I did so.

I was now free to teach full time. I did go back to school and earned the credentials that allowed me to teach in public schools and in the community colleges.

The varied assignments I took on gave me room to learn and to grow, as well as to serve. My psychology degree came in handy when I taught in a locked mental hospital. My "students" were on the verge of being released to society. They needed to learn about acceptable and unacceptable behavior. This was a serious challenge because of the nature of their illness. At times, it was dangerous. It was also satisfying. I used role-playing techniques and got dialogues going. I brought teddy bears to class, to talk to, to hug, and to be friends. The patients voiced their hopes and their fears. Some made it outside, and some did not. I hope they learned from me, because I certainly learned from them.

In 1991, I suffered a severe stroke. I could no longer work. The people at the hospital, staff and patients, wrote to me, visited me, and gave me courage to go on. As I had tried to teach them about life, they taught me about survival. I am grateful. My students didn't want another teacher, and my class simply did not go on.

The stroke was devastating. It was months before I knew, for sure, that I was going to make it. It was then I started reviewing my life's work. The teaching memories were the best. I looked back with fondness at my time with the Fremont and San Jose Unified School Districts, with Condie College, and West Valley Community College. I remembered my time as a substitute teacher in elementary schools. I gave classes in mathematics, adaptive geriatric education, navigational engineering, electronics, yoga, tai chi, wine appreciation, employment skills, history, math, biology, mental health, couples therapy, and massage techniques. What a life! It was full and it was fun.

Now, as I contemplated my own recovery, I became convinced I would have to go on teaching and learning in order to feel alive. I had to learn to swallow, to breathe, to eat, to talk, to move and walk and do things for myself. I am now learning how to drive. I had to learn all of this as a person with a disability.

To prepare for my new tasks, I went back to school to complete the doctoral degree program I had started before the stroke. I earned my Ph.D. after my stroke, and I will complete the work for an Ed.D. soon. Before the stroke, I was specializing in sexuality and aging. After the stroke, I added a new emphasis, sexuality and disability.

Now I write on the subjects dear to my heart. I speak to disabled groups, and to people who work with the disabled or who live with them. I talk to doctors, nurses, and therapists.

I address classes whose students will be working with the disabled. My mission is still to teach. I have learned that one never knows whom one will reach.

Recently, I met a woman who had read one of my published articles. She had read it on a plane, coming to San Jose from Los Angeles. She looked me up to tell me how my words had affected her. She had suffered a spinal cord injury and thought she would never again have anything to live for. Somehow, she found strength within herself and decided to confound the experts by healing herself. She does walk today. My article, she told me, reached her in places she knew personally.

Today she has returned to school, is an effective advocate for the rights of the disabled, and looks forward to becoming a lawyer in order to do even more in the community. We have become friends, and I know I am richer for having her in my life.

My life has prepared me for what I am and what I do now. I am an outspoken advocate for the disabled. Many years ago, when I was a human factors engineer, I designed equipment and devised methods for making human beings safe and productive in the space around earth. Now I look for ways to make human beings, although disabled, safe and productive in society on earth.

My Life with Cats

There were periods in my life without a cat. Those times were pleasant, but not as memorable as the times in my life with a cat.

My earliest recollection of a cat goes back to when I was a child. I wasn't named after him, but I was young enough to think maybe there was a connection. After all, he was called "Old Tom." He was gray, black and white, and very scraggly. He was also very mean. He believed that anyone who didn't belong in our yard had to die. These interlopers included other cats, dogs, rats, mice, and even people.

Vivid in my memory is the day of the "great dog kill." My dad's friend was visiting and had brought his young German police dog. They were near Old Tom's favorite lounging spot. My father, noticing Old Tom getting ready to pounce, told his friend to protect his dog from attack. The friend wouldn't believe the cat would attack a much bigger dog.

What followed wasn't pretty. Old Tom landed on the dog's back, viciously biting his neck. The poor dog dropped dead even as the cat continued his attack on the dog's jugular. I well remember how shocked the adults were. I also remember how afraid I was.

He was a big cat about two or three times the size of a normal one. Nobody petted him, or came close, because everybody in our household knew his nature. His worth lay in his protecting our hen house. And if no creature came near the chickens, they were safe.

From time to time, my father tried to lose him. Dad took him away, twenty miles away, and let him loose. But Old Tom was like a boomerang. He always found his way back. Each time he came back, he was meaner than when he left. He made the Guinness Book of Records. He lived to be more than thirty. We heard about that from the people who bought our house and were unable to dethrone him from his barnyard kingdom.

I have no "fond" memories of Old Tom except that I incorporated him into stories I told my kids. He became James Bond in cahoots with a mouse and had many adventures, especially in cheese factories. In my stories for the kids, he became a Disney-like hero, a good guy cat. I realize he served me well.

Tofu was another cat I lived with. He was a Siamese with unlikely coloring: black with white paws. Tofu was smart and agile. He could do tricks, like flipping head over paws in mid-air. I also had Labrador living with us. Although the Lab was much bigger, Tofu terrorized him, sometimes not allowing the dog access to his own sleeping basket. Had the Lab but known, he could have swallowed the Siamese in one bite. He either didn't know or was too afraid to try. He finally was smart enough to disappear.

The cat I lived with the longest was a tan and white Siamese cross. I had become a wine lover and gave my cat the improbable name of Pousse-Fouille as a tribute to a great beverage. She had a sweet nature. She had no voice, so she never meowed. She appeared to have been abused when a member brought her to our church. I fell in love with her and brought her home.

Pousse was an adept mouser, but she lost her battle with a raccoon. The veterinarian who treated her said she was lucky to be alive. She had to wear a collar for the injuries on her neck to heal and large patches on her rear where she was badly bitten. Somehow, she managed to heal and stayed with me for many years. The early abuse and the injuries did not stop her from being a loving companion, until a cancer took her life. My veterinarian had her buried in a pet cemetery.

I missed her companionship. She was a comfort to me when I was sidelined by a stroke, which left me in a wheelchair. I remember her now and smile at her antics. She delighted in bringing me presents from the yard. These included dead birds and rodents. She learned how to open the folding doors to my study. Her antics in running back and forth, first pushing and then pulling at each side of the door, were fun to watch.

I waited a year before finding another cat. For a while, I felt it was too much extra trouble for me and my caregivers to look after a small animal. But my companion sensed my loss and gave me a kitten for my birthday.

One of our friends acts as a foster mother to the kittens left at the local humane society. She called to say she had wonderful new kittens needing adoption. It was a surprise gift for me, but I got to pick from the litter. We have formal adoption papers and had to sign a pledge that we would treat him humanely! Of course!

He was six-weeks-old when he came to live with me. He was a ball of black, white, and yellow fur and soon found the top shelf of my chair-side table to cuddle in. I tried other wine names for him but none seemed to fit. He answered to anything anyway, so it was no problem for a while. Then, one day, his foster mother said "Oh, I just called him T.K. for Tom's Kitty." Well, that did it. T.K. he has been ever since.

He's big now and no longer fits into the top shelf of my table, but he doesn't care. He heads for that spot and squeezes in anyway. I have had to move my usual papers and remote controls out of his way. Somehow I have trained him by training myself to change.

This training has included giving him three different spots for his food, water, and litter box. He sleeps in the garage at night so he doesn't awaken us with his demands to cuddle right on our faces.

He has facilities in the master bath, because that is the

only room with a door we can shut when we want him out of way in the rest of the house. The second bathroom also houses his food and litter box when, most of the day-time, he has free roaming rights. He loves to chase moths, jumping high in the air to catch them. He loves to sit by the computer screen and follow the cursor, not only with his eyes, but also often with his paws. The television is of no interest except we once found him imitating a ballet dancer by stretching on his hind legs and moving in time to the music. Although he is an indoor cat, he watches birds and squirrels in the yard and visits with the neighborhood cats that come around.

My study is off-limits to him, when I am fast enough to keep him out. Fortunately, he hasn't learned how to open the doors yet. What he does in my study is play "kitten on the keys" and, more alarming, he attacks my collection of stuffed teddy bears and owls. I call him a serial killer.

I knew I missed Pousse-Fouile when she died, but I didn't know how much until T.K. came to live with me. Although I remain active in my post-stroke days, there is still much time that can be lonely. T.K. fills that void for me. He is a companion, silently at times, just by being there, and in joyful leaps when he is playful. I also acknowledge that he gives undemanding love when he kisses me, licking my face, even when it's not dirty. It's nice to have a friend.

Tom's kitty, "T.K." rearranges the files.

Conclusion

Understanding that people with disabilities are people with the capacity to love and to care for others is a radical first step.

Once accepted, several others follow immediately after: the ability to love forces a view of a handicapped person as an emotional equal.

An emotional equal is a political equal, so that if people with disabilities can feel to the same depth as you and I can, then we need to look at our programs and approaches in new ways.

—HINGSBURGER

To Be Continued

The road I have traveled was not easy. At times it was not hard. It was just the road. I accepted what I had to, and when possible, I made choices.

I remember once wandering along the Oregon coast, finding a beach full of colored pebbles. I collected them. Later, I polished them in a tumbler, shook them up, banged them around, and when I took them out they were beautiful. And I knew then that agitation can be magic. It is what transformed the humble stones into gemstones.

So it has been with these stories. As a stroke survivor I have done a lot of thinking. I have had ideas and experiences. I have always been a storyteller and teacher. My partner Bobby, retired from work as a lawyer and judge, was suddenly a caregiver as well. Together we have had tales to tell. She brought to our team her early background as a journalist. In a sense, I was responsible for the pebbles and Bobby did the polishing. We hope the reader will receive them as our contribution to a world in which disabled and temporarily able-bodied persons live in harmony, understanding, and mutual esteem.

In my musings, I have attempted to convey hope and to issue challenges. If this also inspires, then I am rewarded.

This is my story. I talk about fear, depression, and a way to choose. I believe that life is motion. It is forward motion. There is no standing still. We can either grow or we can decay. This applies to physical, mental, emotional, and spiritual growth. I have learned many lessons. Thoreau voiced the hardest, and best lesson: "Nothing is so much to be feared as fear."

I talk about attitude. People have said to me they would rather be dead than be paralyzed by a stroke. I do not take kindly to such talk. To me, life is precious, and I doubt them when they say they would choose death. I only wish they are never faced with the question.

The stroke took a lot from me. I miss many things. I loved to hike and to dance. I can't do either now. But I can toddle along in my Jazzy chair. I can listen to music and feel the rhythms in my body.

The stroke gave me a lot. New opportunities. I had been afraid of horses until I met a few I could ride for therapy. I learned the computer and have an active correspondence with friends around the world.

I have met wonderful people in the disabled community. It was after my stroke, at age 64, that I completed my dissertation for my doctorate degree. I started writing this book at age 65, and now, having passed 70, I am getting ready to publish it.

The stroke did not interfere with a lot of things. I have always enjoyed sex, and still do. I am fortunate to have a partner to love. As a psychologist specializing in sexuality, aging, and disability, I try to contribute my academic as well as my personal experience to the subject. I write and lecture whenever asked. I am gratified to see the subject becoming less taboo. National and international conferences on human sexuality have focused mostly on AIDS, the disease, and aids to sexual prowess. Yet, recently, the subject of aging, disability, and sexuality was put on the agenda of a professional seminar.

It was at a lecture in San Francisco that I saw Ram Dass, a teacher I had long admired and known slightly years ago. This was shortly after his stroke. We talked about our experiences and he called me his fellow "stroker."

That word is not in my spellchecker, and it made me think. We need a new vocabulary to describe ourselves. I don't like "handicapped." It derives from the phrase "cap in hand," To me, it is degrading. It implies begging. I am not particularly fond of the word "disabled" either. It sounds too mechanical. Radical activists offer the word "crip." It used to be that "cripple" was a derogatory term. Now, I am not so sure. Calling a spade a spade is okay. Euphemisms are not okay. Labeling is not okay. We are persons first, perhaps with a disabling condition. If we keep looking, we will find the word, and the way to see ourselves and be seen by others as individuals.

Ram Dass dubbed us all fellow strokers. We are, in one way or another. A fellow in our fellowship, Helen Keller, reminded us that life is a glorious adventure. A bold adventurer, Don Quixote, dared us to dream the impossible dream. An inspiring spiritual tells us to keep our eye on the sparrow. I raise my glass and join in Tevye's toast to life and add: "Go for it!"

Appendices

Speak Up: Letters that Worked

1. About Speech Therapy

*I*t has always been important, in my recovery, to be vigilant and alert to any situation that would set me back.

One such instance is reported in the following letter, written to my physician, about my speech therapist.

The result was fortunate for me. A new therapist was assigned, and I continued to work and to improve. I do not know what happend to the therapist after my complaint.

⤳

Dear Doctor:

Almost since my return from Sacramento last year, I have been receiving speech therapy through (our plan). Lillian (name changed), M.A., has been my therapist. Until recently, I had felt both Lillian and I were doing well together. She was encouraging and I was encouraged. I could tell my speech and swallowing functions were improving. My friends also noticed the changes.

However, several weeks ago, she started saying I was not improving, and since six months had passed, there was little chance I would improve. She accused me of "not cooperating."

This hurt, since I have worked very hard in speech and all other therapies. No one has ever said I did not cooperate. I am even enrolled in swim and physical education classes, all at my own expense.

Lillian also indicated she did not believe me. For

example: You referred me to the "throat" specialist. He was heartening when he told me I was doing very well, that my vocal cords were "symmetrical" and I could look forward to continuing improvement. When I reported this to Lillian, and brought her a note from the doctor to that effect, she indicated she did not believe me and would contact the doctor herself. I do not know if she ever did that.

As recently as two weeks ago, she reviewed the audiotapes she had made of my voice over a period of time and pointed out the audible improvement.

Since she will be leaving soon on maternity leave, we have been discussing her replacement for me. At all times she said she would continue until she left and then turn me over to the other therapist. When she later indicated her dissatisfaction with my progress, I asked if she wanted to drop me. She said that she would continue until she actually left and then there would be a replacement. Nevertheless, yesterday, in her office, she told me she was going to recommend no more therapy for me, with anyone.

It is hard to reconcile her statements, and even harder to understand why she is now saying what she is saying. I have cooperated in every way, doing the exercises she suggested. I have only questioned her when she said that after six months, if there were no significant improvement, then there would be none in the future. I questioned this statement because of my own experience to the contrary, and because of the extensive literature on the subject. I know, and I am sure you do, too, that one cannot say when improvement will occur in the stroke survivor. No deadline can, or should be, placed on recovery.

More important, the negative finding can result in great harm to the stroke survivor. Hope should never be taken away. This is especially damaging when the judgment is made on no evidence other than a statistical "norm." I do not see how she can dispute the medical findings on the state of my vocal cords. She has given me no contrary evidence other than her "professional" evaluation. On what grounds? She says only that "six" months is the criterion.

I therefore ask that you authorize speech therapy for me with another therapist at the earliest possible time. I assure you that I will continue to do my utmost to maximize the therapy, as I have done since I started on this slow but increasingly progressive recovery.

Many thanks for your assistance.

Sincerely,

/s/Tom Matola

cc: Therapist Lillian (name changed), MA

2. About a Doctor

Six months after my stroke, a few months after leaving the hospital, and only a short while into therapy, I was evaluated at Kaiser by a physiatrist, a doctor specializing in the treatment of strokes using special equipment or physical and occupational therapies. It was the only time I have ever seen such a specialist.

When we met she didn't rise from her desk where she was engrossed in paper work. Without looking at me, she very matter of factly announced that I would never get any better. Her reason: it was six months and statistics showed that after six months little recovery could be achieved. Although I was stunned, I told her she had a right to her opinion and I had a right to mine, and I didn't agree with her.

The truth is I was devastated. After all, she was the oracle, the specialist. It took a few days before I could recover. I knew I would have to do something to overcome her prognosis, because she had the power to cut off my therapy. What I did was send a letter, a copy of which follows.

The day she received it, she called. She apologized. She said she hadn't thought about it from my viewpoint. She asked for another chance to be my doctor. After much thought, I agreed.

It turned out well. I feel she learned something so she could help other patients, and she and I went on to develop a working relationship, which helped me on my recovery. When I moved out of the area, and saw her for the last time, she said she was "impressed" with my progress and continuing recovery.

Did I help make her a better doctor? I don't know, but she had the power in her to change and it is my belief it was for the better.

⌣

Dear Doctor:

I am informed you are the person to whom this complaint should be addressed. I write on behalf of Tom Matola, as his friend and attorney in fact.

The complaint concerns Dr. D (name withheld), who was assigned as Tom's physiatrist (when he entered a rehab facility).

Tom had a severe stroke on September 21,1991. He has made significant progress in recovery, and we know he still has a long way to go. We also know that he is strongly motivated to achieve as much recovery as possible. He works very hard and has always cooperated with his doctors and therapists, and, until the incident of which I write, they in turn have been helpful not only with medical advice and treatment, but with encouragement. I cannot stress enough how important that last element is.

On April 7th Tom kept a routine appointment with Dr. D. She began by asking him to read an article written in elementary English. She never explained her purpose. To Tom, it was insulting, since he never had any difficulty in reading or in comprehending. His eyesight was not affected. His mind was not affected. Tom holds masters degrees in psychology and is a Ph.D. candidate. Her manner was condescending, at the very least. More importantly, it gave the impression she didn't know anything about the patient she was addressing. It appeared she had not even read the correct patient file.

We had a number of questions; important to the patient, about feelings he was having in his affected arm and leg, including some pain. Although asked several times, she avoided giving any answers or even acknowledging that the questions had been asked.

After watching him walk, and saying he had made a lot of improvement, she told him that his condition was "essentially stable" and he couldn't expect any more "significant improvement" in his affected right leg, and the arm was given a worse prognosis. She said that physical therapy would not help. She said he was "permanently disabled" and that we should contact the

State Department of Rehabilitation. She did say his speech would probably improve and therapy would be helpful for that purpose.

When questioned as to why she made such statements, she repeated several times that in stroke cases, after six months, when there was no more progress than what Tom showed, the prognosis was poor. We told her we had learned that significant improvement could and did occur 18 to 24 months after the event. She then questioned the source of our knowledge and I pointed out to her that it was written in large letters on a sign hanging in the patient day room at the Medical Plan's Rehabilitation Facility. Tom told her she was entitled to her opinion but he was entitled not to accept it.

And accept it we do not. There is too much evidence contrary to her opinion. There is certainly evidence that the belief system plays a large part in a patient's recovery. Dr. D was remiss in delivering her opinion as fact. She was also remiss in overlooking the damage she might do to her patient. In fact, Tom left her office and became depressed, a condition he is still fighting. Although his blood pressure has been controlled under medication, it shot up immediately after the visit and is only now showing signs of returning to stable.

While Tom is strong and independent minded and capable of recognizing that doctors can be wrong, he still suffered from what he perceived to be a callous disregard of his interests. He had questioned her prescription of a metal brace in heavy shoes. She ordered it for him, and to be cooperative, he had been using it, even though some of his therapists questioned the necessity for it. Tom feels it is archaic. In the stroke group exercise class he attends, no one wears such a heavy brace.

He has stopped using it, returning to a plastic brace, and has discovered that his leg had weakened. He is practicing with the plastic brace again, and finds that his leg gets stronger. He feels that the use of the heavy brace contributed to atrophy of his leg muscles.

Since her arrogant dismissal, Tom has started swim therapy. His therapist has found significant improvement in three weeks. He now walks out of the pool, without a brace or shoes. He feels movement in his right arm, using it in the pool to support his exercises. The therapist tells him he has much potential for recovering.

I am told that Dr. D might have been concerned about patients who are in "acute states of denial," and that she didn't want to raise hopes. I assure you that had Dr. D taken the time to learn about Tom, talked to his therapists, or to me, she would have learned otherwise. We are both highly educated, reasonable, and, we feel, realistic people. We know that Tom may not recover fully. We are prepared for that eventuality. We are not prepared to give up hope, or give up our efforts to do everything necessary to see that what recovery is possible, will be achieved.

I had the impression that Dr. D was concerned with cutting off physical therapy so that (the medical plan) would not be liable for the cost, and that her statements were to justify that end. We do not accept that conclusion from her unsubstantiated statements, when even their own facility talks of recovery occurring up to two years after the stroke.

We do not admit that Dr. D was correct in her opinion, and further, even though she may have believed it was correct, we feel she had no right to present it the way she did.

Tom will not return to her care. She has admitted she can't help him, that she can't see him getting any better. We therefore ask that another physiatrist be appointed. We also request that her denial of further physical therapy be set aside, and such therapy be allowed.

Don't Pull The Plug

We will appreciate your prompt attention to this matter. Thank you for your courtesy.

Sincerely,
/s/Roberta Johnson

cc: Dr. H.E. Social Worker

Recommended Reading

Stroke

Berger, Paul F., and Stephanie Mensh. *How to Conquer the World With One Hand, and an Attitude.* Virginia: Positive Power Publishing, 1999.

Buckman, Dr. Robert. *What You Really Need to Know About Caring for Someone After a Stroke.* New York: Lebhar-Friedman Books, 2000.

Das, Ram. *Still Here.* New York: Riverhead Books, 2000.

Klein, Bonnie Sher. *Slow Dance.* Toronto, Canada: Random House of Canada, 1997.

Mantle, John. *Cyclops Awakes.* South Carolina: Lucky Press, 2000.

McCrumb, Robert. *My Year Off.* New York: Broadway Books, 1998.

Newborn, Barbara. *Return to Ithaca.* Rockport, Massachusetts: Element, 1997.

Rocket, Dr. Howard, with Rachel Slate. *A Stroke of Luck.* Toronto, Canada: Parnassus, 1998.

Disabled: Important Insights

Anderson, Hoyt. *Accepting Disability.* Sacramento, California: Disabled Resources Services, 1994.

Blanc, Joanie, ed. *Still Doing It: Women and Men over 60 Write About Their Sexuality.* San Francisco, California: Down There Press. 2000.

Charlton, James I. *Nothing About Us Without Us.* Berkeley, California: University of California Press, 1998.

Fries, Kenny, ed. *Staring Back.* New York: Penguin, 1997.

Janus, Sharon. *The Magic of Horses.* Hygiene, Colorado: Sun-Shine Press. 1997.

Kroll, Ken and Erica L. Klein. *Enabling Romance.* New York: Harmony Books, 1992.

Maxfield, Georgie. *The Novel Approach to Sexuality and Disability.* Sparks, Nevada: Northern Nevada Amputee Support Group, 1996.

Mooney, Thomas O., Theodore M. Cole, and Richard A. Chilgren. *Sexual Options for Paraplegics and Quadriplegics.* Boston: Little, Brown and Company, 1975.

Olkin, Rhoda. *What Psychotherapists Should Know About Disability?* New York: The Guilford Press, 1999.

Russell, Martha. *Beyond Ramps.* Monroe, Maine: Common Courage Press, 1998.

Shapiro, Joseph P., *No Pity.* New York: Random House, 1993.

Sife, Dr. Wallace, Ed. *After Stroke: Enhancing Quality of Life.* Binghamton, New York: Haworth Press, 1998.

Association of Swimming Therapy. *Swimming for People with Disabilities, second ed.* London, 1992.

Essays Published

A Winning Combination
Sports 'n Spokes, Sept./Oct. 1995: p. 35.

Acceptance is not Defeat
Stroke Connection Magazine, Fall 1996: p. 6.
San Jose Mercury News, Oct. 17, 1996: Celebrations p. 17E.
Catch the Wind, March 1999: pp. 3 – 4.
Betty Wright Swim Center News, November 1996: p. 1.
Be Stroke Smart (National Stroke Association), May 1996:
Vol. 13 no. 5.
Stroke Connection Magazine (National Heart Association),
Fall 1996. Vol. 18 no. 4, p. 6.

Aging, Sexuality, and Disability
Catch the Wind, December 1999: p. 5.

Change of Life
Betty Wright Swim Center News, Dec. 1997, p. 3.
P/N (Paraplegia News),

Color Me Please
P/N (Paraplegia News), April 1999: p. 74.
Catch the Wind, Mar. 1999: pp. 3 – 5.
Mouth, June/Aug. 1999: p. 22.

Dancing Horses
Active Living, Nov/Dec. 1998: p. 10.

Disabled Make the Best Lovers
Enlighten, Dec./Jan. 1997: p. 8.
Catch the Wind, July 1, 1998: pp. 2 – 3.

Don't Box Me In
Catch the Wind, April 2000: p. 6.
P/N (Paraplegia News), April 2000: p. 66.

Dying to Live
  Enlighten, Dec./Jan. 1998: p. 12.

Fear
  Catch the Wind, Nov. 1998: pp. 5 – 6.
  P/N (Paraplegia News), Jan. 1999.
  Be Stroke Smart (National Stroke Association), Feb. 1999.

Fuzzy Creatures I Have Known
  San Jose Mercury News, February 5, 1998: Celebrations.

Hippotherapy: Two Views
  Strides, Oct. 1998
  Catch the Wind, Oct. 1998: pp 1 – 3.
  San Jose Mercury News, Oct. 8, 1999: Celebrations.
  Be Stroke Smart (National Stroke Association), Aug. 1997.

Hooray for Sex
  Family Synergy, May 1999: pp. 9 – 10.

Horseback Riding as Sex Therapy
  It's Okay (Canada), Winter 1996: p. 11.

If I Can Ride a Horse, I Can Do Anything
  EFMHA News (Equine Facilitated Mental Health Association),
July 1998.

Lab Rat
  Catch the Wind, Mar. 1998: pp. 3 – 4.

Look Who's Talking
  Catch the Wind, April 1998: pp. 1 – 2.

Perchance to Dream
  New Mobility, August 1999.

Sex and a Stroke
  It's Okay (Canada), Summer 1993: p. 3.

Stroke: A Bird's Eye View
Topics in Stroke Rehabilitation, Winter 2001: pp. 61 – 63

Swim Therapy
Betty Wright Swim Center News, Dec. 1998: p. 3
Catch the Wind, Jan 1999: pp. 2 – 3.
Enlighten, February/March 1999.

Taking Risks
Catch the Wind, Feb. 1998: pp.1 – 2.
TBI Challenge (Brain Injury Association), Oct. 1998: pp. 1 – 2.

Teddy Bear Therapist
Catch the Wind, May 1999: pp. 3 – 4.

Tom the Teacher
Catch the Wind, May 3, 1998: pp. 3 – 4.
P/N (Paraplegia News), June 1998.
Enlighten, June/July 1998: pp. 21 – 23.

What to Do After the Doctor Leaves
Enlighten, Aug./Sept. 1998: pp. 1 – 10.
Catch the Wind, Dec. 1998: pp. 1 – 5.

What's Wrong with Vanilla Sex?
Family Synergy, Sept. 1996: p. 1.

Who's Afraid of the Big Bad Horse
Be Stroke Smart (National Stroke Association), Aug. 1997:
p. 1 – 3.
Kanganews (NCEFT), Summer 1996: p. 1.
Strides (NARHA), Fall 1997: p. 2.

You Can't Get There from Here
Catch the Wind, Oct. 1999: pp. 5 – 6.

The authors at a wedding after the stroke

Biographical Sketches

Thomas Matola, Ph.D.

Dr. Thomas Matola, a retired psychologist, sexologist and teacher, now spends his professional time lecturing and writing. He also rides horses, surfs the net, gardens, swims, works out at the gym, and is a "lab rat" for experimental stroke therapy programs. He still likes to hug. He also loves the opera and Shakespeare.

Still recovering from a major stroke that hit in 1991, Tom is an active advocate for the disabled. He has become a facilitator for motivating others in their rehabilitation efforts. He lectures and writes about sex and the disabled as well as about sex and aging.

A native of the Bronx, New York, he received an M.A. in Industrial Psychology. He came to California in 1962 and worked for Lockheed as a Human Factors Engineer in the space and submarine programs. His exploring mind and interests led him to work in private and public endeavors. He has taught in varied fields: tai chi, meditation, survival skills, grade, high school and college subjects. He also worked as a therapist in a mental hospital and as an associate professor in colleges. Before coming to California he had careers in banking, law enforcement, and in the Air Corps reserve as a navigator and navigation engineer.

The San Jose City Council has recently appointed Tom to a four year term as a commissioner on the Disability

Advisory Commission. He also serves as an adviser and activist in numerous organizations: Saratoga, California YMCA; West Valley College, Peninsula Stroke Association (affiliated with American Heart Association), Center for Independent Living. Tom is a member of the SSSS (Society for the Scientific Study of Sexuality), American Association of Disabled Persons, the National Stroke Association, and the Council of California Adult Educators. He has appeared at Stanford University, San Jose State University and other campuses. He has been a featured speaker and panelist at Lifestyle conferences.

In addition to publishing articles in periodicals, Tom has contributed chapters to two books: *Still Doing it!*, edited by Joanie Blanc; and *Magic of Horses*, edited by Sharon Janus.

Before the stroke Tom was a candidate for the doctorate in education at the Institute for the Advanced Study of Human Sexuality in San Francisco. Three years after the stroke, in 1994, Tom was awarded his Ph.D. from Summit University. Tom's creed is to keep moving and doing with life what is meant to be done with it. Live it!

Roberta Johnson, J.D.

Roberta Johnson, in retirement now, writes, lectures, works crosswords, reads mysteries, indulges a passion for Shakespeare and opera, and most of all is an ardent hiker. She also works part time as a Judge.

Since her companion suffered a stroke in 1991, she has become a "caregiver" and an activist for disabled rights.

Born in Brooklyn, New York, she attended high school, college and law school in California. Unlike the lady in the song, who is a tramp and hated California, Roberta loves California. She worked her way through college as a newspaper reporter and editor, did a stint in radio news in Hollywood, earned a Juris Doctor at Hastings College of Law in San Francisco. She has worked on political campaigns, as a lobbyist in Sacramento, practiced law, and spent more than 25 years as an administrative law judge. As assistant chief of her agency she was in charge of training judges. She taught in law school and was on the faculty at the Judicial College in Reno, Nevada and was a founding mother of the California Administrative Law College.

Barbara Heine, P.T.

Barbara Heine was the founder and executive director of the National Center for Equine Facilitated Therapy in Woodside, California for many years. In the winter of 2000, she left to return to her native Australia. She had served as a mentor, teacher, trainer and therapist in many capacities. She also served with the American Hippotherapy Association and the North American Riding for the Handicapped Association (NARHA).

Sharon Janus

A humanities and literature professor, Sharon Janus has studied the honored role of horses in both Greek and Native American cultures for years. Her own experience with her thoroughbred mare, Sibernet, led her to investigate the healing relationships shared between people and their horses. Horse-crazy all her life, she now lives in Colorado with her husband, son, two horses, three dogs, and two cats.

She is the author of *The Magic of Horses,* published by SunShine Press Publications, Inc. in 1997, in which the article "Healing Through Empowerment" appeared.

If you liked this book and would like to pass one on to someone else, please check with your local bookstore, online bookseller, or provide the following information:

Name _____

Address _____

City _____ State _____ Zip _____

Don't Pull The Plug _____ copies @ $12.95 each $ _____

California residents, please add applicable
    sales tax $ _____

Shipping $3.50 first copy,
    $1.75 each additional copy $ _____

Total enclosed $ _____

For more than 5 copies, please contact the publisher for quantity rates. Send completed order form with your check or money order to:

      Intrepid Press
      PMB 142
      15559 Union Avenue
      Los Gatos, CA 95032-3904

      FAX: 408-559-8212
      PH: 408-559-4440
      E-MAIL: iintrepids@aol.com
      WEB SITE: www.dontpulltheplug.net

International shipping is extra. Please contact us for the shipping rates to your location, if outside the United States.